JUNK MALE

ACKNOWLEDGEMENTS

*I have received terrific 'unofficial' help and advice
from many people but would particularly like to thank
Olivia Deighton, Nicola Faulkner, Juliet Cahill and
Jack Barendse and, of course, my parents.
However there was also an official squad of three:
to Paul Colsell, my marvellously wry illustrator;
to my friend and editor, the indefatigable Emma Donald;
and especially to me go great wafts of gratitude.
We have had masses of fun and quite a lot of wine.*

JUNK MALE

Alasdair Romanes

ILLUSTRATED BY PAUL COLSELL

NormAl Services

WANTAGE, OLD WINDSOR AND WHITE WALTHAM

Text ©2009 Alasdair Romanes
Illustrations ©2009 Paul Colsell

First published in Great Britain in 2009 by NormAl Services

The right of Alasdair Romanes and Paul Colsell to be identified as
Authors of the Work has been asserted by them in accordance with the
Copyright, Designs and Patents Act 1988.

A CIP catalogue record for this title is available from the British Library.

ISBN 978-0-9563493-0-9

Typeset in 11.2/15pt Bembo by Paul Colsell Creative Services
Printed and bound in the UK by European Print Group

Any similarity between the characters and any persons living or dead is
entirely accidental, although the misguided think Roseman is modelled
on the author. God forbid! His life is, his views and attitudes are not.

...Beautiful Catholic Church in Wargrave

1984

I am, as you will all remember, a man of brilliant mind and original ideas and as I sat watching Coronation Street last night, yet another new thought flew into my head: would it not be a marvellous idea to send all my friends an annual letter updating them as to my latest adventures? Now that the heady days of university are receding into the misty past, I seem to see too many of you too rarely which must be hard for everybody. So my Christmas Letters will serve a dual function; you will discover what cards The Fates★ have dealt me, whilst simultaneously enjoying the fluent writing style that the Edinburgh tutors so appreciated in my four year stay in Auld Reekie. Not for nothing did they award Alasdair Roseman a 2:2 in Geography and African Studies.

I am certain most of you know that this year saw Samantha Trout and me tying the knot. On a drizzly, grey June day we were joined by no fewer than 25 friends and relations in the not exactly beautiful Catholic Church in Wargrave. It was such a pity that over 100 people were unable to attend for a variety of remarkable reasons—poor old Johnny Derdle!—but perhaps, had the Trouts had a full house at the reception, the floor of their upstairs sitting room would have given way earlier and the applause following the end of my speech would have gone through the floor, rather than through the roof. We disappeared to a self-catering villa on the South Coast for a five day honeymoon which gave Samantha a taste of her future life, lucky girl. I, meanwhile, am worried by the taste that I was given: she really will have to up her game if meal times are not to be such an ordeal! I can, of course, turn my hand readily to *haute cousine* but that would be to deny Samantha what is almost her birthright. 'Woman, know thy place,' is the motto in this family.

My career in the City as a stockbroker with Laing and Cruickshank, where I sat on the European desk, had been extremely promising in its

---

★ A gruesome Greek clique of three who were good at handing out misfortune. Hence the phrase you may have heard of: A *Fate Accompli*.

early weeks and in late October I almost sold some shares. My heart was, however, not really in the financial world and when the Head of Institutional Sales called me in to see him one November morning, I had to let him down by announcing my intention of leaving the company.

Whilst this must have been a terrible shock for him, he bore it bravely and succeeded in hiding his disappointment beneath a fixed grin. He even opened a bottle of Champagne to lessen the blow. I suspect that the imminent Big Bang will be just a little muffled following my departure—a damp squid more like. The City will of course eventually recover from my exit, but don't expect a Bull market until 1991 or so. You heard it here first.

So what now? Well, never being one to waste a moment, I immediately telephoned my old school, Donnington Grove, where my uncle happens to be on the Board of Governors. The Head, who remembered my brother well, immediately offered me a post as a French teacher, and Samantha is to be an Under Matron. She has therefore had to bring a close to what she, a trifle delusionally, called her 'burgeoning success' as a PR Consultant with Head, Strong and Smart. She lacked some of her usual understanding when I broke the news to her. I explained to her that things could be worse; she might become ill 'Andropov'—a bit of wit always lightens these situations I find. Perhaps the fact that we will be staying in a charming old cottage with Norman the music teacher will cheer up the old Trout! So here we come, Oxfordshire. I have always said that what matters most in life are the three Es: Education, Endeavour and Eggs. Incidentally, I shall not be wasting my time with any teaching qualifications as we great teachers are born not made.

In this Olympic Year I was disappointed that the Ruskies chose to boycott Los Angeles; would we or the Americans have done the same to them? I think not.

My own sport remains of a high standard and Samantha has felt the power of my squash racket periodically—her 'sprained' wrist has not, in my humble opinion, adversely affected her performance and only by exercising the deuced thing was it going to get any better. 'Play up and play the game,' I urged her whenever she tried to employ gamesmanship by requesting a break. Typical of the fairer sex to try the 'but I feel faint' card when they're losing.

On the football field, the Old Wykehamist 2nd XI has had an inordinate number of matches called off, it seems, and I have starred only once. A fixture previously cancelled was miraculously reinstated only 24 hours before kick-off. Despite thinking that I would be otherwise engaged, the captain, Roddy Paxtell, almost begged me to play, when I fortuitously bumped into him at the off-licence, such is the esteem in which he holds my talents. We lost the game but I can safely claim that the fault was not entirely mine. As a goalkeeper I cannot be expected to catch the ball every time; I model my game on that of the continental keepers and punch threatening crosses as if they were thugs demanding my money. It is not always easy to land a punch.

Samantha is out watching *A Passage to India* at the cinema with some old acquaintance but I know what is important and insisted on staying behind to write our first Christmas letter. It is very much in my nature to let my 'little lady' enjoy some freedom and I trust that she appreciates her good fortune in having landed a catch of such quality. I hope you all have a fantastic Christmas. God bless you.

Alasdair and Samantha

1985

This year began with Samantha and I finding ourselves spending New Year's Eve stuck in my car outside the Natural History Museum. I drove our Renault 4 up to London for the Trafalgar Square Celebrations and left it parked in Exhibition Road from where we caught a bus. Unfortunately, Samantha was at her scattiest worst and failed to turn the headlights off, so the battery was flat when we returned at 12:30 a.m. The AA, an abominable organisation, only deigned to pitch up at 3:30 in the morning by which time we could have been extremely chilly. What a night!

We are delighted to let you know that at the end of September, Sam gave birth to our first child who has been christened Kensington. He is a strapping lad and took some time to emerge but, fortunately, the John Radcliffe* has an excellent café and I was able to spend some relaxing hours there, waiting for Mrs Roseman to do what she's paid for! Actually, after three hours I returned home as the highlights of an important football match were on the television and I did not want to miss the rare opportunity of watching City grace the nation's screens. Emotionally intense experiences are always followed by peaceful slumber and so it was a restored Ros who returned to the JR in the morning to find what the stork had deposited.

Life at Donnington Grove has been exhausting for us both but the matrons do at least have three hours off in the afternoon whereas we, the real staff, are at it non-stop. I have been hard at work revising and improving my French; thus I will be able to pass on my expertise to the boys and *j'ai ne trouvè pas que difficile.* To be honest, as we grow older, learning comes to us with greater ease than it did in our youth. I worry about my pupils though; they seem to be struggling a tad. If only they listened more attentively and left their petty squabbles outside the

---

* Oxford's hospital which is named, I believe, after Canada's official hangman from 1892 to 1911.

WHAT A NIGHT!

classroom, they might find progress *'plus bon'*. The Head seems to me to be stuck in the dark ages; not much sign of *Glasnost* or *Perestroika* there! My insightful advice is seldom acted upon, which may well end up costing the school dear. I never have a clue what is going on from day to day; it is almost as if it were deliberate.

The school management is not totally without vision, fortunately, and I was put in charge of the Under 10 side for all sports. They are, I am assured, a talented bunch but we were consistently unlucky throughout the year and did not record a single win. I shouted at the players a great deal but they were not to be motivated. Boys of today do not appear to have the fire in their bellies that burnt in mine when I was their age.

In July, Samantha went to the Live Aid concert organised by that rather unappetising and hirsute fellow, Bob Geldof. He clearly is only interested in self-promotion and probably doesn't even know where the country of Africa actually is. I doubt that we'll see him on the charity bandwagon again. Samantha certainly came back full of it (I think we can all agree that women tend to be ruled by their hormones at the best of times and more so than usual when they are pregnant) but I maintain that charity begins at home. We should be much more concerned about the hole in the ozone layer opening up above Antarctica. I know it will never close but we must try to ensure that it does not grow any larger. Incidentally, I do not feel it was sensible for a woman the size of a house to go jigging about at a popular music concert but despite my banning her, the old Trout sneaked off. (I knew that it was a mistake to let her omit the 'obey' clause from the wedding vows.) Sam, foolish thing, certainly is into youth culture at the moment; she recently played me some rubbish by a girl who calls herself Madonna (what blasphemous cheek!) who will soon disappear into the obscurity from which she arose, mark my words.

Kensington's arrival has meant that I have had to make some decisions about Samantha's life. She has allowed herself to become sloppy in her household duties whilst the loss of her figure is a trifle embarrassing for me. Her New Year's Resolutions are that she must take more exercise, wear more supportive underwear and use her time off to clean the

communal kitchen and sitting room more effectively as dear Norman, the music master who shares the cottage with us, has a lot on his plate.

Our summer holiday was spent on the South Coast at Hythe where we spent our honeymoon. We met a charming couple called Bob and Maisie who run a kennel down there. They are both in their fifties but Bob is a real hoot after a Babycham or two. The weather meant that we had to stay indoors a lot but Bob kept us entertained and taught us how to play whist. In fact, they have invited us to go on a whist drive after Christmas and although Samantha seems a little bit stand-offish, I have said that we will go. We also found a Bingo Hall and 'House' became the cry with which our English 'gang of four' greeted each other every time we met. I have had some T-shirts made with 'The Hythe Housers' emblazoned on them and will present them to B & M at the whist drive.

It is a pity that we saw so few of you in the course of last year although I'm sure that I caught a glimpse of my Best Man, Simon 'Tucker' Turquet, outside the Pavilion at Lords. It would seem however that age is beginning to affect his hearing, for my bellows of 'Tucker, you F★★★★★!' went unanswered. It was his loss as he was unable to benefit from my observations as to how the game was going. On that subject, had Edmonds and Emburey given the ball the sort of tweak that I give it, the result might well have been different. Anyway, Happy Christmas to one and all and I hope you all have a better year than Rock Hudson and his aides had last year! My legendary wit, you see, remains undiminished.

Alasdair and Samantha

STAFF AND CHILDREN ARE BEGINNING TO RESPECT ME

1986

I have had a year in which I have been dogged by ill health. Many of you will know that I suffer my illnesses with staunchness and I tend to play them down, even though I have had more than my fair share of problems since birth (when my umbilical cord* had a go at me). This past 12 months has, however, seen me struck down by sickness and diarrhoea and I am, to boot, beginning to lose my hair. I hate alarmists but it has just crossed my mind that the nuclear accident at Chernobyl may, allied with the wrong type of winds, have something to answer for. I would be delighted to receive correspondence from any of you who have experienced similar traumas so that I can build up an overall picture.

Samantha and I have, nevertheless, been able to pack in a plethora of activities and chief amongst these has been our purchase of a small cottage in the little village of West Hackthred. (Great Aunt Greta—yes, the bearded wonder herself—passed away and left me a little dosh; those three visits I paid her were worth it after all.) Norman is going to lodge in the spare room whilst Kensie will share our room. Sam reacted rather coldly when I suggested that Norman should move with us but I explained that if the poor fellow stayed at school he would end up having to tidy his own room and the kitchen, which would be terribly emasculating for him. He has, as I may have previously mentioned, a lot on his plate. Commuting is something of a problem as we have but the one car. Fortunately Norman and I work very similar hours and Sam is able to make use of the excellent local bus service. Kensington travels with her to work where she dumps him in the sick bay—provided that I am not already in temporary residence there. I have thoughtfully bought Sam one of those baby strap-on thingies as her Christmas present!

In recent weeks, the old Trout has cheered up for no apparent reason and even the death of our three Angel Fish did not diminish her *Jour de*

---

* Umbilical 'chords' are sometimes mistakenly defined as the absurd screams of pseudo-agony given during childbirth!

vivre (spot the French teacher!). The fish tank was knocked over by my son and heir as he crawled around our domain while we were all out in the garden. We returned to find a flood and the corpses of Ange and Gel on the carpet; of Fish there was no sign. Poor old Kensie put a brave face on it, but clearly the trauma of the episode played havoc with his constitution, for he had terrible wind for the rest of the day. Meanwhile, Samantha has landed a small part in the village Christmas show which is directed by a dashing fellow called John F Gribley. Ever the conscientious lass, she is rehearsing madly but I hope that the house will not consequently start looking a mess.

School life has been entertaining and I believe that staff and children are beginning to respect me. I even have a nickname—SS—which stands for Super Sir if I am not mistaken. A colleague suggested it stood for Space Shuttle as I am supposedly always exploding in class. This is tasteless humour and anyway, one has to keep a tight rein in lessons, I find, and if I shout occasionally, it is only to make myself heard. Educational busybodies have changed our French syllabus so that the children now actually have to speak the language, as well as undergo terrible things called aural comprehensions. This has made life most difficult but I now begin every lesson with a cheery *'Bonjour'* and finish with *'Avoir'* so I suspect the pupils are well on their way to fluency. Monsieur Prescemort, Head of French, seems unworried although he has been off sick much of the year. The Under 10s secured a victory in the rugby season against St Michael's, who were such a rude ill-disciplined bunch that very quickly I had to send three of them off.

My own sport is at its usual high level although I only starred once for the Old Wocs, when I was asked to don my gloves while watching a game in which our keeper broke his nose and came off with five minutes left. We almost held on to our three goal lead but not quite. Well, I must dash as I need to see that Sam has started supper for Norman and me. I wish you all a *'Joyaux Noelle'* and urge you all to raise a glass to the late great Harold Macmillan over the holidays.

Alasdair, Sam and Kensington

1987

This has without doubt been the most dramatic year yet in the life of the Roseman family—it is difficult to know quite where to begin. I suspect that we are on the road to great things; we, like the FA Cup winners Coventry City, are setting out on a journey that will see us, like them, covered in glory over the next two decades.

Let me begin with the beating heart of the family—myself. In September, in the very first week of term, Monsieur Prescemort, the Head of the French department at Donnington, dropped down dead and I was appointed Head of French.

What a stroke of luck!

Under my aegis★ I had a department of one—a new teacher—which soon became two when a replacement for Prescemort was found. I am worried about both of my charges who seem to have little idea of how to teach: the old new teacher, Madame Dublanc, plays the children cassettes all the time whilst the new new teacher, Graham Davison, makes himself foolishly popular and the boys actively look forward to his 'buzzy' lessons. (There's no buzziness like show-off buzziness!) Successful teaching, and I speak from experience, depends upon the pedagogue dominating the pupils and ensuring they know they are to be quiet and submissive. We, the professionals, do not need their unformed and ill-judged opinions; I spend a good 40 % of my timetabled periods with all Year groups arguing about this. Modesty prevents me from inviting Ma Dame and Mon Homme to observe one of my lessons. *Je detester 'le buzziness'*.

★ Originally a cape worn by people to show that a bunch of holy do-gooders was on their side—in the manner of Batman.

Samantha enjoyed her very small rôle in West Hackthred's Christmas show last year but John Gribley the director, fine fellow though he is, did go miles over the top when he described her as the next Marilyn Monroe. I don't want the old Trout getting ideas above her station. For her own good, I told her that realistically Hatty Jacques was more like it. If I ever become as pretentious as John do let me know.

Anyway, back to our triumphant year; not long after Christmas, Antha did in fact begin to look like Hatty Jacques and, in late May, she gave birth to our daughter, Fou Fou Latte. I love the name as the first two words sound so Gallic, whilst the third adds an air of Italian mystery. Antha said that Frances was a better choice and that John thought so too—quite what John has to do with it I do not understand. Well, as a fair man, I compromised and said that if we had another boy we might call him Francis.

I'm sure you will be wondering what an extra child meant for our delightful lodger Norman, the music teacher. The children obviously couldn't both sleep in our room so I have suggested that with the money we inherited from Great Aunt Delilah, we should build a new bedroom on the ground floor for Norman! The works have already begun. In the interim, Antha and the children have moved into the spare room and Norman has moved into our room. Fear not, we have a solid bolster between us on the bed! If we didn't, the whole situation could be deemed a little bizarre!

So new responsibility, new baby, new extension to the cottage—there was not a hint of bad news for us. My parents could not make the same boast: on the 13th October they claimed a 'hurricane' uprooted a tree in their garden and replanted it in their kitchen. I would have gone over to help them but the Under 10s had an important match coming up and I knew where my loyalties lay. I also have to feed Kensie's rabbit every day as his first one, Fluffy, last year's Christmas present, escaped when Kensington was feeding him and was run over by a milk float. We wouldn't want that to happen to Bunnykins. On the subject of Kensington, our long wait for his first words came to an end about the

We Wouldn't Want That to Happen to Bunnykins.

same time as Fluffy did: he uttered 'squashed'.

I think I saw dear Tucker Turquet, my Best Man, at Henley this year. I shouted at him but the deafness I noted a couple of years back must really be taking a hold. I gather he married last month—he must have lost our new address. Samantha spent the October half term on a camping trip with John and Norman in the Lake District while her parents looked after the children. I, meanwhile, went to visit Bob and Maisie and then joined a soccer tour with the Old Wykehamist 3rd XI but sadly did not get a game. When I returned home, I found a sick Norman in bed having had to return early from the Lakes. Poor chap and poor John and Antha!

How good it is to have Maggie back for a third crack of the whip. What a girl!

Alasdair, Antha, Fou Fou Latte and Kensie

Norman Suspending his Dislike of Davison

1988

L ast year was a breeze but 1988 proved to be a temporary glitch in the endless success of the Roseman clan. Things began badly in the spring term at Donnington, with Graham Davison being asked to take over the running of the French department. This was a strange decision for the Head to take as I had just begun to lick things into shape and young Davison is distinctly callow. Davison has been insufferable ever since and had the audacity to suggest that the quality of the boys' French results was down to him. Well! This bunch of candidates has been at the school as long as I have and one always expects immense improvement in the final year—I had laid the foundations. Davison also has the brazen cheek to call the Head 'Pete' in a wanton display of lack of respect; to me, Mr Whindin remains and always will remain 'Headmaster'. I am not a bitter man but if the publication of *The Satanic Verses* has led to a fatwa being issued on Salman, Davison's arrogance is worthy of the same treatment.

The boy Norman moved into our completed extension in April and has asked whether we could possibly install a kitchenette to make things easier for him. I see no reason why this should not be feasible and it is important for Norman to be happy as he has a lot on his plate at Donnington. I am certain that Norman disapproves of Davison but Normy is such a good egg that he even manages to suspend his dislike enough to go to the pub occasionally with GD (I think that stands for Great Dolt—Roseman's subtle humour remains undiminished!). GD was also asked to run the Under 10s cricket which I had dealt with, in understated fashion, for four years. Needless to say this group was genuinely blessed with natural talent and proceeded to enjoy an unbeaten season. I did give words of advice from time to time to their captain, young Stebbington-Brush but, typically, GD failed to acknowledge my assistance.

The completion of Normy's glorious extension freed up the second side of my bed, but I suggested to Samantha that as the children are still so small, they really need a parent in their room. I would have offered my services, but I need my sleep and have again been suffering from poor health. Thus it is with great reluctance that I have given her the privilege of caring for my little Fou Fou Latte★, and Kensie of course.

Samantha is still working in the undemanding post of Under Matron and takes the bus to work every day with the bairns. How lucky she is not to suffer the desperate daily stress and tedium of being behind the wheel. Little Wifey was also asked to join the Parish Council at West Hackthred and, needing to fill her time, accepted. She now sits on various sub-committees with my great friend, John Gribley. I made it a condition of her accepting the post that the cottage and extension should continue to look clean and tidy and so far so good. It remains to be seen if she can maintain the standards over Christmas and the New Year, as she is Cinderella to John's Prince Charming in the village show.

'How are the children faring?' I hear you ask. Their fortunes have been mixed: Kensie struggles nobly whilst Fou Fou shines. We bought a parrot called Perkins for Kensie early in the year, in the hope that it might encourage the lad to speak a bit more but this did not transpire. Soon both Fou Fou and Perkins were speaking with far greater fluency than he. Perkins' progress came to a grinding halt when he was let out of his cage one summer afternoon and was tethered to a garden chair; Kensington never saw the poor bird as he shot round the corner on his tricycle. Our boy's vocabulary was however sufficient to inform us of the accident: 'Squashed againy'. Fou Fou can already walk and talk with some confidence and has starred in a series of baby commercials. She has beautiful eyes, a divine giggle and fine features—very much her father's daughter. When I remarked upon this to Sam she agreed, 'Oh yes, Alasdair, you are so right'. She is a decent lassie.

My sport has been limited this past 12 months due to a calamity that befell me at the tail end of the skiing season; I was trying to demonstrate

★ I have nearly had my fill of a woman at the grocer's who insists for some unfathomable reason on calling our little angel 'Mad Mad Milk'. I suspect that you would struggle to find a name like that in the Birth Announcement columns of *The Times*.

to the wife and John on the slopes of Wengen that I could jump as far as that chump, Eddie the Eagle. A strong gust of wind caught me as I flew over the mogul and the ligaments in my ankle were probably torn on landing. I returned home to join the children in the care of my in-laws. Consequently, my tennis has been limited and I became something of an armchair sportsman enjoying Ben Johnson's flying Olympic 100 metres. I believe the drug he was really on must have been Speed! Ha Ha! So another year has vanished into the ether without my seeing Tucker, Johnny or any of you lads and laddettes—with the notable exception of Bob and Maisie. Let's put that right soon.

Alasdair, Antha, Fou Fou Latte
and Kensington

1989

It was not just the Berlin wall that came down this year; we had the misfortune to have a lorry crashing into our sitting room in early April and down came the wall, rendering my bedroom above it temporarily unusable. We subsequently had some reorganisation of sleeping accommodation to do, as Norman had been difficult since the New Year. He had left me stunned when he announced that the ghastly Graham Davison was moving in with him. I was reluctant to cause more friction by asking him to vacate the premises for which he pays no rent as he has not much on his financial plate. Consequently, I had to move into Samantha's room where we and the children did not really have room to swing a cat. Thus it was fortunate that Toshka our new kitten had passed away in the accident that caused all our problems. The repair work has recently been finished along with a second floor to Norman's extension which he told me was an absolute necessity. I said that I would prefer to save some of my grandmother's legacy★ but Norman retorted that he had always considered me a friend yet was beginning to have his doubts. I could have responded with the same tyranny displayed by the Chinese authorities in Tiananmen Square but I do not want to be tarred with that particular brush. I am, as you all know, an intelligent democrat.

I am sure that you will all be desperate to know how things are going at Donnington Grove. It has been a quiet year for me but I am now showing that I am a pony with more than one trick and have been teaching Latin instead of French. GD reorganised the French department and announced—*paix possibler!*—that my services were no longer required. This is yet another example of his high-handed approach but was a blessing for the beleaguered Latinists whose Head of Department had just been appointed to a Headship in Hampshire. (I myself had considered applying for that post, but loyalty prevented me.) Luckily for everyone

---

★ Money that those of us from the upper echelons of society are often bequeathed★★.
★★Given by the dead.

OUR NEW KITTEN PASSED AWAY IN THE ACCIDENT.

involved, I was prepared to turn my hand to a little bit of the old Classics. Great teachers can pass on their knowledge in any subject and I did secure a grade 6 in the 'O' Level back at Win. Coll.

Most exciting has been my promotion to coach of the 2nd XI cricket. It was a pity that the first team coach—a crotchety old-timer called Herbert Waslin—decided to train the top 22 players as a squad thereby leaving my expertise lamentably underutilised. Nevertheless, despite his domineering approach, the lads and I managed an excellent and unbeaten season with two wins and ten draws. It is sad how many opponents failed to take up the challenge of a fair target and how several others expected us to go on outrageous run chases.

Manty has become Head Matron having done a First Aid course over the summer break. This allowed me to visit Bob and Maisie in their camper van down in Woolacombe. We had a glorious week of Scrabble, Cribbage and Whist and Maisie taught me how to crotchet. The children were, as ever, glad to be with their grandparents.

Despite Kensington's speech coming on in a leap and a (rather small) bound, he was cast as third sheep in the Donnington nativity play. He performed the rôle with his own, Modernist interpretation—namely that the sheep was worried that Jesus was cold and needed his fleecy comfort in the manger. Parents expect too much of children and many suggested to me that Kensie should have been withdrawn as, allegedly, he had been fighting in the majority of rehearsals. I believe they were jealous that he stole the show with his magnificent and amusing butting of Joseph. Fou Fou Latte has been in terrific form and is already reading at just over two years old. Her conversation is sparkling and her favourite programme on the television is the News. Her modelling career is time consuming but rewarding financially.

Manty has been busy on the Hackthred Parish Council which seems to have meetings lasting late into the night at least twice a week. I do admire the public spiritedness that she and my dear friend John Gribley show and they were wonderful as Maria and Captain von Trapp in the village show of *The Sound of Music*. I offered my services as Stage Manager but they both were adamant that I worked quite hard enough as it was and should remain at home relaxing with the children. Next year is my 30th birthday and I enclose an invitation for my party which, as you will see, is to be in the charming village school. Donnington, Headmaster Whindin told me rather aggressively, does not allow staff to use its facilities—I believe he should 'wind in' his neck! (Word play at its best!) I am hoping old Tucker will make a speech in response to a few well chosen *bonnes mots* of mine and Johnny Derdle is never one to miss out on a bash. Be there or be square.

Alasdair, Manty, FFL and Kensie

1990

How wonderful it was to see so many of you in February for my big day! Thirty years of almost constant success is something for which I am both modestly grateful and, gratefully, modest. Some of you, I know, failed to make the select guest list (better luck next time). Others were unable to attend due to a series of unfortunate events (including poor old Normy, out and about in Reading, who couldn't find his keys). Thus for all of you disappointed friends out there, I had better give a flavour of the occasion, so you know what you missed. Let me just say this, I overheard more than one departing guest proclaim that the evening would be etched on their minds forever.

The 31 of us gathered in West Hackthred village hall, where the musically-based celebrations began with my 11-year-old nephew, Sebastian. After just five years of lessons, for a boy of that age to give a ten minute violin recital and produce sound like that is quite something, as I heard one or two guests murmur. One even said that he liked it as much as he did the bagpipes.

There was then a heart-rending solo from Bob—one comment I heard aired was how his gravelly bass voice, only hampered a little by a hacking cough, made him the ideal vehicle for the ultimate romantic ballad, *Lady in Red*. But best of all, was the stunned silence which greeted Maisie when she actually did bring out the bagpipes and we were transported to another planet.

Domino's Pizzas did the honours for food and a series of fruity white German wines graced our palates. We then watched a spectacular indoor fireworks show before I made my speech. I had not realised how much 45 minutes of oratorical hilarity could take out of you. As you know, I seldom, if ever, blow my own trumpet, but I must admit that I was rather proud of my little joke about Bob's HACKing cough being appropriate for a musical spectacular in West HACKthred! It still makes me chortle today. My parents sent a video message but, unfortunately, after 20 minutes

THE EVENING WOULD BE ETCHED ON THEIR MINDS FOREVER

battling with the video player, the tape was eaten. This hiatus* had a benefit as it provided me with the opportunity to recite this, my poetic tribute to my first 30 years:

Old Roseman is such a grand chap;
His jokes they flow as if on tap.
Women look at his form and sigh—
For a smile from him they would die.
He is unassuming and modest,
Talented, clever—just the best;
When he strides into any bar
The clients stand and shout hurrah.
Old Roseman is such a fine chap.

For any aspiring poets among you I suggest that you note how this opus has a subtle circularity. It takes skill and practice but persist and you may eventually approach my standard. Anyway, I am sure you will be keeping your diaries free for my 40th.

Manty has had an exciting year. Firstly, she and John Gribley were chosen to represent the village skiing team in the annual competition against East Hackthred, which took place in St Moritz. We won and so are the holders of the inaugural Thredders Trophy. Hurrah! Gribbers and Sam then launched a chic children's clothing shop in Oxford called 'Trout's Sprouts'. I have to admit that initially I was not convinced about the sanity of this idea, as Manty would have to leave the safety net of the school salary behind her. But, once I had analysed the economic climate, I realised there could be no better time to go into business. (Never forget my successful career in the City and my innate financial acumen.) It was even I who penned the shop's rather natty little name. Of course, although I have allowed Manty to get out of working for a living whilst she plays at shops, I will not let her evade her household chores with quite such ease. Trust me, give the little woman an inch and she'll want a mile.

Meanwhile, life at Donnington goes on in thrilling fashion. I now

---

* A break, as in the hiatus hernia I would suffer if I endeavoured to pick up a pregnant Samantha.

teach Latin to the beginners rather than to the top classes. It was felt by the new Head of Department that those at the beginning of their classical education needed someone of my pedagogical pedigree to steer them through the minefield that is *Mensa* and *Amo*. I love it and sometimes find time in lessons to entertain the little fellers with tales of my holidays with Bob and Maisie. The 2nd XI cricket was unable to repeat its heroics of last year, but my magical touch secured a triumphant season for the tennis team which I now run alongside the coach. Graham Davison's self-promoting style is the only blot on the landscape and I personally believe that Deputy Head may be an appointment too far for him. I have seen men of his ilk fall before—*on vas voire!*

Talking of the dreaded GD, I am pleased to report that Stormin' Norm'n and he are no longer living together in our extension. They had a terrible row shortly after my party—I heard the words 'Reading' and 'cheap' being tossed around with gay abandon—and the next day, Davison was gone. Normy and I are back on terrific terms—reunification has been a theme of the year—and I sometimes have supper with him in his kitchenette, when he's not at his evening classes in Reading, that is. I imagine when Nelson Mandela left Robben Island he must have had the same sense of release as I did when GD left my abode.

The children continue to prosper: Kensie repeated his year in Reception and is now quite loquacious, if admittedly a touch difficult to understand. He had a nasty bout of the pox but we think that he is young enough for the scarring to disappear. He was strangely cast as 'The Prisoner' in the nativity play and spent the entire evening locked in a cage. I cannot say that I know the Bible well but I think he played his part convincingly. Fou Fou Latte now reads fluently and is beginning to speak French to Madame Dublanc who still plays her infernal cassettes at school. She also suffered from chicken pox but had just a handful of spots on her back which soon vanished. She runs around the school charming one and all. I am so proud: she is a chip off the old block. In the words of the immortal Jim Henson who died just recently: '*That's all, folks!*'

Alasdair, Manty, Fouffs and Kensington

BEING A MEMBER OF THE WEAKER SEX

1991

A Merry Christmas and with it I, like the Queen, shall give you a message to take to heart. Samantha and I have never been other than disarmingly modest about our remarkable achievements and those of our brilliant progeny. Personally, I cannot bear the tenor of those Christmas Round Robins that brag about so-and-so's child and their manifold deeds of excellence. Truth, not opinion, is what I seek in a letter and truth is what I give. Forgive my preaching but my clear vision undoubtedly needs to be shared.

Our news this year revolves predominantly around Fou Fou Latte, our little genius of a daughter. She began school this past term and, like cream, she rose quickly to the top. Competition is a dirty word in education these days and rightly so but Fouffs is the cleverest pupil in her Year by absolutely miles. Her reading age is twice that of her peers; her arithmetic is, I would hazard a guess, keeping her teacher on her toes; and she speaks French nearly as well as I do—*chique allors!* She watches the News every night and is generally astute, although she did suggest the other day that Bush and Co should have pressed on into Baghdad—a smidgeon naïve, but she is only four. The Iraqis will oust Saddam without our help, that's for certain. Fou Fou's modelling career knows no bounds and she is earning good money which, on her behalf, I had invested in 'Trout's Sprouts'. There is even a possibility of a rôle in the summer in the TV series *Why don't you turn off your television..?* Despite all her success, she remains a level-headed little girl with looks to kill for.

Kensie finds life a little more of a struggle but nonetheless shows great determination in all he does. He is a terrific animal lover and last Christmas we gave him a pair of hamsters which he cared for with religious fervour throughout Boxing Day. Unfortunately, in early January he put their cage into the garden and the next morning they were two little blocks of ice. Fou Fou tried to lay 'healing hands' on them but to no avail. Poor Kensington! I think he deserves a dog.

Not unsurprisingly, Samantha and John's children's clothing business went bankrupt in November. I believe I had warned them on several occasions that recession was looming and I am a little cross that poor Fou Fou has lost all her money. Perhaps they will listen to me in the future as I am an experienced student of the economy. The question we now face is what Sam can do with her time; both children are at school. She would be on an almost permanent holiday were she not to return to work. My friend Gribley, not dismayed by the demise of 'Trout's Sprouts', has offered her a position in his marketing company but Sam is reluctant to join him despite her having the necessary qualifications. I cannot understand her as she spends so much of her time with John anyway. My New Year's resolution will be to persuade her to succumb to his proposition with gusto.

This year I prevailed upon Sam to join Bob, Maisie and myself on a week's break in their caravan in Southend. We were unlucky with the weather but we played a lot of whist and went to the Bingo Hall most afternoons and evenings. It is a thrilling way to pass the time and I would thoroughly recommend it to you. On the final night, Sam took us all to see *The Silence of the Lambs*. Being a member of the weaker sex, Maisie was terribly frightened and collapsed in the Picture House. It transpired that she had a weak heart and all those of you who have met her will be sad to hear that she passed away shortly afterwards. Bob has since remarried Heather Smithson, an old friend of Maisie's. Whilst I think about it, we never did find out what happened to old Lecter; answers on the back of a postcard, please.

On the subject of postcards and holidays, Sam and John repeated their Thredders Cup skiing triumph of last Easter but this time in Whistler. Freed from the shackles of married life, I offered my services to the Old Wykehamist soccer side as a referee on their tour to the North of England. I am a firm wielder of the whistle and brook no dissent, thus I had little choice but to dismiss four opposition players in the opening game. Our lads followed the school motto: 'Manners makyth man,' and kept all 11 on the pitch and battled to a superb victory. Much to my disappointment, I was not called upon to officiate again, although I kept the players amused on the coach journeys with my much-anticipated Quizzes and renditions of Frank Sinatra classics.

It has been a quiet year at Donnington although my coaching prowess has been duly noted and rewarded. The Under 9 (1st !) soccer team has been given into my tender care. Had our two fixtures not fallen victim to the weather, we would indubitably have conquered all, what with Archie, the youngest Stebbington-Brush, as our skipper.

GD, my nemesis*, has been revelling in his position as Deputy Head and would have it that our numbers our holding up purely due to his inspirational ministry. His leadership is reputedly as 'buzzy' as his French lessons—well, if that is the case then I wish that he'd BUZZ off! (Oh the joy of a quick wit.) He certainly lacks management skills on the football field as his 1st XI almost lost to Grasswell Hall—a terrible establishment hardly worthy of being called a school! Meanwhile, Normy's music department is flourishing and he is in fine form, enjoying a few private clients in Reading every week. I hope you all like the surfing turtle on our Christmas card—so much jollier than some of those dreary Mother and Child ones. Season's Greetings to you all.

Alasdair, Normy, Samantha, Fouffs and Kensington

* An arch-enemy—as Professor Moriarty was to Sherlock Holmes, so Davison is to me.

37

I HAD NOT SKIED OFF PISTE BEFORE

1992

I t has been an *annus mirabilis* for the Rosemans; we have so many of them that it is positively embarrassing! My excellence as a sports' coach was rewarded in September when—following the peculiar disappearance of the previous incumbent, Trevor Garden—I was appointed Head of Sport at Donnington. This is a demanding position requiring the organisation of Fixtures against other schools and the timetabling of our sporting day. It took me several hours to sort everything out but I am not one to shirk responsibility. Garden, it recently emerged, had been involved in some credit card fraud. This does not surprise me as I had never trusted or liked the man—some of you may have met him at my exclusive 30th birthday party a couple of years ago. He was the incompetent who oversaw the swallowing of the video tape. Need I say more.

The school proceeded to enjoy a triumphant soccer season in which not a single fixture was lost to the weather and only occasionally did opponents arrive to discover that our team had gone to another school. I am loving encouraging and correcting the coaching techniques of colleagues who are not as gifted as I.

Clearly my own side, the Under 9s, suffered as my time was taken up with pressing matters and they did not manage a win but played in exuberant fashion. The whole school—except perhaps GD—look forward to the Roseman years as the boss of Games. Incidentally, I do not think that I am revealing any big secret when I tell you that Mr Whindin is retiring as Headmaster. I may only be 32 but I am going to apply for the job and I am confident that my business experience in the City will count in my favour. Stand by for great news!

Sammy has thoroughly enjoyed working for John Gribley's company and was as happy as I have ever seen her in the first couple of months of the year. To complete her joy, I decided that this year I would join them on their skiing venture in Wengen and that the children would come too.

They sweetly suggested that Bob might take it amiss if I did not join him and Heather for an Easter trip to Bournemouth; I explained that Bob might like a little bit of space in the early months of his new marriage. Not everyone has my sensitivity.

I had not skied Off Piste before but took to it very quickly and soon I even heard John praising me as being 'a powder elephant'. Kensington was less of a natural and regrettably broke his arm on the first morning and had to be looked after by Sammy at our hotel—none other than the famous Park Hotel! We met a delightful couple called Grant and Mary Thorn and as Grant had a torn calf muscle, he kept Sammy company. Mary, meanwhile, shot off round the pistes with John while I spent a short spell teaching Fou Fou Latte. Fouffs was a brilliant little skier and so I enrolled her in ski school—she won a prize at the end of the week and made a short speech in German (!) to thank her instructor, Hans. The only drawback to the holiday was that the other adults seemed to enjoy smoking the weed; I pretended to but I did not inhale. Back at home, Fouffs has continued to excel academically and she was also *Victor Ludorix* at our school sport's day. She is popular with everybody and took it upon herself to help Kensie with his reading; he has made incredible progress and his speech too has become much clearer. They gabble away all night in their room and are inseparable. Together they are looking after our new tortoise, Tipper, and he has been with us for eight months now, which is the longest we have kept any animal! Kensie did try to float him upside down (he may become a boat designer in later life) in our ornamental pool but Fouffs came to the rescue. I must buy them a dog. News of Normy is that he is in rude health and is very happy and continues his one-on-one's in Reading. His musical leadership at the school is exceptional and the parents and I admire him immensely.

Whilst I referred at the start of this letter to our *annus mirabilis*, it would be remiss of me not to tell you that my own health has again been a little worrying. I have had stomach pains and thought for a while that I might have an ectopic. These pains subsequently died away but I have been reluctant to participate in much sport as a result. The young American Agassi, who preened his way to the Wimbledon championship this year, should be grateful that I am not a few years younger and that I am cursed by injury and ill health. Of course, time away from the sports field has permitted me to pen some remarkable poetry including this powerful work:

> *Anguish, pain, aches and hurt*
> *Soreness, fear, health alert*
> *Stomach throbs and head it spins*
> *Through all this a brave man grins.*

Finally, just yesterday I received a Christmas card from Johnny Derdle who is now living in New York and is working in finance. I thought I had better correct those of you who assured me that his abode was in a little village near Newbury. I knew it could not be the case as I had sent endless Christmas cards to the address I was given and yet never received one back. If any of you are around my way this Yuletide, do pop in—you might just be lucky and see John and Sammy playing the leads in an adaptation of du Maurier's★ *Don't Look Now* at the village hall.

Alasdair, Normy, Sammy, Fouffy and Kensie

★ A fantastic author whose works include The Three Musketeers (or something similar). Recommended reading!

1993

I can hardly bring finger to keyboard to write this Christmas letter as I have little but bad news to bring. If Her Majesty—God bless her—thought she had it bad last year, in relative terms she had a barnstormer of a 12 months. I have been looking for an Oscar Schindler-type figure to rescue me. Only strength of will, fortitude and irrepressible spirit have kept me going as one misfortune has followed another.

In January, John Gribley ran off with Mary Thorn. One evening he was chairing the Parish Council meeting and the next day he was gone. 'What,' I asked Samantha, 'does he think he is doing?' She replied that she could hardly believe that he would vanish without a word to us. Thus I was astonished when scarcely a week later I returned home to find Sam's clothes gone with her in some of them. There was a note on the kitchen table which boldly announced that she had decided to live with Grant Thorn in a Romanian orphanage, that she loved him very much and that I had never cared for her. How can she have said that? I have given her the freedom to embark on her own business ventures, have allowed her to holiday without me and have ensured that she kept up high standards of housewifery. She is an ingrate*, I am well rid of her and I will never take her back. Her departure is no more than a hiccough in my life.

Unfortunately I seem to be suffering from the hiccoughs, for in April it was announced that Graham Davison would be Donnington's new Headmaster from September. I had high hopes that I might have been given the nod and my interview went superbly. I spoke of traditional values, of keeping parents at arm's length, of putting fussy mothers right and of sport as being the only vital element of extra-curricular education. The governors did not even have the perspicacity to place me on the short list. To then appoint GD ,who is a mere whipper snapper of 32, was to compound their folly. The fools! What would happen to the school I love? Well, at the end of the Summer term (in which there was some

---

* Selfish, ghastly, awful, foul, loathsome, lacking in gratitude.

THERE WAS A NOTE ON THE KITCHEN TABLE

minor confusion over cricket fixtures and some unpleasantness between myself and the staff of several schools), GD called me into his office and informed me that I was being dismissed! Laughably the words 'Gross incompetence' passed his lips! He has no understanding of what makes a superb teacher let alone a brilliant schoolmaster—and the two are not the same. Donnington has come to rely on me and the day that I departed, three separate boys, including Stebbington-Brush, came up to me and said life would not be the same without me. That is a vindication of all I have aspired to achieve in my time at the fine establishment.

In my hour of need I turned for support to Norman, my greatest friend, and this is when I began to feel how David Koresh must have done at Waco: under attack from all sides. Norman announced that he too was leaving Donnington and was moving to Reading where he had found a new job and new love. Within a week, Norm's extension was empty and I was alone with the children.

For the first time in ages, September saw me unoccupied and when Fou Fou Latte and Kensington returned to school—my mother is paying the fees—I was truly on my own. I am fortunately an imaginative fellow and soon found work peeling off bark in a walking-stick factory. It may be said that this does not keep my enormous intellect satisfied but I am building a body which the ladies, whom I am now at liberty to chase, will find hard to resist. Returning home one day, I spotted Johnny 'New York' Derdle in Newbury and stopped to have a chat. He was over from the Big Apple for a couple of days and on hearing of my misfortunes he said, 'I don't know why you don't get a damned job on the radio so you can tell the world about it.' He is full of good advice; I have sent a demonstration tape to Radio 5 and expect to hear from them in the New Year.

So there is hope on the horizon and Fou Fou Latte received great accolades for her performance as Mary in the school nativity. It was not ideal that Kensie had covered much of her face in indelible black ink as she slept the night before, but the school painted her entire face black to hide this and her beautiful singing voice had, Madame Dublanc told me, the audience in tears. I was not able to witness this first hand: I was requested not to attend as it could have caused embarrassment and, being a decent cove, I did not. Fou Fou also won prizes in every subject and continues to tutor Kensie in her leisure time—consequently he has nearly caught up with his peers. Sadly for Kensie, he was recently doing water displacement in science at school and decided to continue the experiment with Tipper the tortoise at home. This time Fouffs was not on hand to save the beast. I trust that you have all enjoyed a better year than Tipper and me.

Alasdair, Fou Fou Latte and Kensington

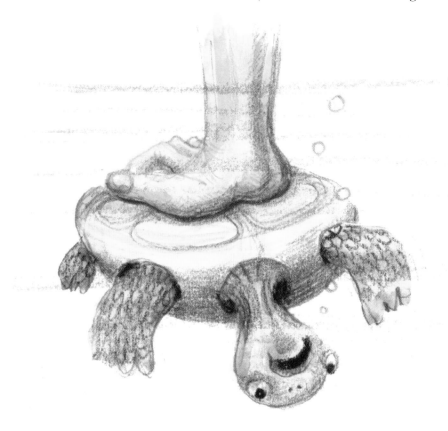

1994

Life never stays grim for too long—a point that should encourage poor Forrest Gump's little brother and what a fascinating documentary that was. They and I have been passing through equally turbulent waters but, at the bottom of the waterfall of misery, lies the calm pool of content. (I think that perhaps I should start teaching English some time in the future.) The early months of the year saw me become a vital cog in the machine that is a walking-stick factory; my attendance in the industrial unit had to be limited, however, as I developed a repetitive stress injury known to me as Peeler's wrist. My colleagues were not entirely sympathetic and implied that there could be other reasons why a newly-single man might suffer such an injury. Imaginative though I am, I cannot think of any apart from a heavy load of washing up. I recently had dinner with Bob and Heather and amazingly it turned out that Bob had once also worked in the stick manufacturing world. What a fascinating evening we all enjoyed as my dear friend and I swapped shop floor anecdotes!

During the time I spent at the factory, I sent off my demonstration tape to the BBC and lo and behold, they sent back a charming letter, complimenting my 'interesting' voice and suggesting I get a little experience in local radio before contacting a national station again. Clearly they wanted me and this will be no surprise to those of you who recall my skills of oratory from our days at university. Suitably encouraged, I contacted an Oxford radio station who almost begged me to come and spend a day at their studios. The day was informative but I cannot say that I would like to have a career working with such bellicose★ people: why they cannot find a simpler way of letting one know that a programme is on air than a silly little red light is beyond me.

I spent much of the spring and early summer employed in a bookshop where my linguistic skills—German and French at 'O' Level—were put to

★ Always sticking one's stomach into other people's affairs.

POOR KENSIE HAD A NARROW SQUEAK

47

good use in the Spanish and Italian section of the Languages department. I reorganised the displays and made sure that neither I nor customers were disturbed by the invasion of men and women who kept coming along to try and sell their books on our premises. I was such a fine vendor myself that soon our shelves were almost empty and it was at this point that, rather than being awarded a bonus, I was asked to leave. Jealousy is a powerful emotion.

Do not worry as you read about The Ros! Fortune favours the brave and in a local newspaper I saw an advertisement for a Science teacher at Grasswell Hall. It is a fine school which I came across while at Donnington; indeed in many ways it might be deemed a superior establishment—certainly that will be the case soon, for I now work there! My interview with the owner/Headmaster, Michael Millicent, went swimmingly and it was extraordinary how many theories on education we share. He is an honest chap and admitted that the recession had reduced numbers but we shall build them up again. The 53 pupils will be blessed by our vision and the roll will swell. As those numbers mount so, Mike assures me, he will be able to pay me a stipend more commensurate with my experience and talent. Much of the summer was therefore spent brushing up on my Physics, which was a challenge in which I revelled. I have also bought some vital equipment such as shoe boxes, Tupperware and elastic bands. The reality of the job has been as terrific as the prospect and the other eight staff, who are somewhat elderly, look to me for leadership.

The children have both enjoyed magnificent years. Fou Fou Latte was spotted at last year's nativity play by the Headmistress of Slatterleigh Park (yes, the Yvonne Warmonckton-Smythe!) and on inquiring about Fouffs, she offered her a scholarship worth—I won't be vulgar and mention the amount—95% of the fees which are currently £2,000 a term at Slatterleigh. Fouffy settled down quickly into boarding school life and as I write has just been awarded the Pendlebury Project Prize. She has also starred in the Under 10s netball as goal shooter despite being two years younger than the other girls. She remains as modest as ever—I wonder who she gets that from?! I was not going to leave poor Kensie at the execrable Donnington and he has joined me at Grasswell where he has matched the other pupils stride for stride. He did have a narrow squeak when the school pavilion was burnt down one afternoon just after he had left its washroom facilities! God fortunately smiled on us this year. As a reward for their fantastic efforts I have bought the children a dog which I have named Wooflemeister. He is a Golden Retriever of inordinate beauty.

So those who deserted the good ship Roseman last year will be regretting their foolhardiness. The Trout is welcome to her thorny fate (my humour never dims) and when last I heard they were somewhere in France near Avignon. I personally do not care where exactly and I hope that the farmhouse 3½ km northeast of the village of Flaux near Uzes is cold and damp. Gribley is, I gather, moving into education but we do not really want him and I doubt that he has the necessary skills. As for Normy there is no news. Incidentally if anyone knows Derdle's address in NY, could they give it to me as I want to ask him about his job which seems to give him endless holidays—I saw him from afar four times in Newbury this year but could not catch his attention from my car. All the best from three of the best.

Alasdair, Fou Fou Latte and Kensington

1995

Samantha has come back to me as I always knew she would! Our relationship is just as good as it ever was, if not better! She arrived at the family seat in West Hackthred one misty morning in March looking dishevelled and not, as I pointed out to her, at all like a Gallic Scarlet Woman. Thorn—a bounder of the highest order—had just upped and left her. We Rosemans have standards and neither I nor Sammykins would ever behave in such despicable fashion. As luck would have it, there was an opening at Grasswell in the Laundry and I insisted that she take it. Although Little Wifey had that ever so slightly down-at-heel appearance, she has put on a few pounds and I merrily quipped to her that she had been seized by a *'faim fatale'*. Oh how I laughed!

Life at Grasswell would have been a challenge for an inexperienced schoolmaster, but it is fortunate for all that I am a master of prodigious and unassailable talent. Whereas the discovery that all the pupils had been asked to leave their previous schools for an assortment of misdemeanours would have floored a lesser man, not so The Ros. I do not want to preach to you but I believe that it is the parents who are to blame; so often they do not see what is going on right under their noses. A firm hand is necessary, sometimes literally, as my own offspring know. Anyway Kensie, as I may have mentioned before, took to the place immediately and won his first ever prize at Speech Day: a commendation for Best Beater at the school shoot.

We both revelled in glory this year as my science teaching received the highest praise from the inspectors: 'Science teaching is alternative and the pupils are more often than not left to their own devices.' That old adage is so true—a child is not a bucket to be filled but a fire to be lit. In point of fact, in May one of the children was actually lit when Kensington accidentally pushed a Bunsen burner across a worktop to where Christopher Dawlish was resting his head to look at the miniature aquarium. My lad saved the day with his quick thinking by emptying the

KENSINGTON ACCIDENTALLY PUSHED A BUNSEN BURNER ACROSS

water over Dawlish. Tragically there was a heavy price to pay for the inhabitants.

But enough of me and my life at Grasswell for I am not a bore. As the academic year drew to its conclusion, new excitements awaited. Fou Fou Latte has proved a terrific hit at Slatterleigh and when Yvonne-the-Head heard that Fouffs' pa was in education, and a language teacher to boot, she demanded that I come and join her cheery band. She interviewed me over the phone and to give Michael Millicent (Grasswell's Head Honcho) his due, he did not stand in my way. Although my loss must have been a bitter pill to swallow, he nobly wrote me what I gathered was a superb reference. It was no less than I deserved. Samantha and Kensie moved with me and Sam is helping to market the school.

I am not, as you know, a man to oversell the achievements of my nearest and dearest, so trust me when I say that Fouffy was the S T A R of Slatterleigh's production of *Jesus Christ Superstar*. She is only eight years old but was cast as Judas Iscariot and gave three performances of a lifetime. On the third and final night Dermot Howlington, who was playing Jesus, had lost his voice but FFL knew his part and carried off both rôles even when the characters were on stage at the same time. I may have said this before but she is a chip off the old block. Samantha has done a satisfactory job as a marketing advisor but I think Yvonne wanted to make her feel good about herself when she told her she was 'quite brilliant.'

We have decided it is time to leave West Hackthred and are looking for accommodation more suited to a family of our social and career standing. We also need a garden in which Wooflemeister, our marvellous Golden Retriever, can cavort with the children. We are looking in the vicinity of Slatterleigh, just north of Newbury. I have my contacts in Estate Agency including my young sister who, unable to stand the pressure of life in the City, bailed out—'Those who can, do: those who can't, sell houses' is, I believe, the saying. Charmaine and I have not spoken for a decade or so following THAT dispute over how eggs should be boiled but I believe the time has come to forgive and forget. It will be sad for the village to lose us but somewhere is about to get a very nice surprise.

Three final pieces of news: firstly Éloise Dublanc, whose teaching I so admired at Donnington, has joined the staff at the Park and has certainly increased the beauty quotient★; secondly, Norman Jones has been back in touch after his betrayal a couple of years ago. He has left the oldest profession in the world and is working for some crockery manufacturers—Fou Fou Latte remarked that he has a lot of plates on his plate now. Lastly, I feel that I should pass on to you the sad information that recently those two genuine Bravehearts, Johnny Derdle and Simon 'Tucker' Turquet, were lost at sea in a yachting accident. I had been trying through my numerous contacts to get in touch with Derdle but all to no avail. Then, out of the blue, his brother (I didn't know he had one, but interestingly the envelope had been posted in Newbury, so he must be local) wrote to break the news—and my heart. Ah well, *c'est la vi* or rather, *la mort*. If you don't laugh, you'll only cry, I say! Get ready for a wonderful Christmas!

All the Rosemans

★ I like to call it the 'Totty Quotty'!

1996

What a year it has been! We seem to have packed 52 weeks of action into a mere 12 months. Most exciting is the news that Johnny and Tucker are alive and what a way to find out! Thanks to my sister Charmaine's rather grudging help, Antha and I succeeded in finding a charming and deceptively spacious period cottage in the quaint village of Aldworth just above Streatley. On the very first night that we were there, we decided to pay a visit to the local pub, 'The Bell'. As I walked in, who should I see sitting at the bar but the ghost of Johnny Derdle. I am not ashamed to admit that I burst into tears and threw my arms around him—we English are becoming less afraid of showing our emotions. Johnny was rather more stiff upper lipped than I but I could see a gamut* of emotions running across his face. He told me that, after floating in their life raft for three weeks, he and Tucker were rescued. It emerged in the course of the next ten minutes that Johnny is our new next door neighbour—oh what good fortune for both families. Johnny is clearly a popular figure at the pub and I gather that he has been 'Clubman of the Year' for the last four seasons at the cricket club. Now that is a mark of the man; for to achieve that while working full time in New York is a remarkable feat. Happily his ex-patriot days appear to be over. When I got hold of Tucker he appeared a little bewildered as to what I was talking about. Their miraculous escape has affected him deeply in my humble opinion. To commemorate their joyous salvation I produced this Wordsworthian verse:

> *The boys they really are back in town,*
> *Gone their youth, their academic gown.*
> *Tucker's fatter, Derdle's lost his hair,*
> *But The Ros remains so debonair.*

---

* Range. For example, I trust you will all widen your vocabulary, thanks to the extensive gamut of words I employ!

THAT INNATE GIFT FOR COMMUNICATION

Dramatic events have unfolded at Slatterleigh too. In January, Yvonne Warmonckton-Smythe announced that she was retiring at the end of the year. I was all for applying for the post, which would surely have been mine for the taking, but Antha pleaded with me to resist as she wanted me to be around for the children. A succession of candidates traipsed around the school during March making obsequious comments to the staff that they met. They were all desperately dull and none had that innate gift for communication that we great schoolmasters have in buckets. The final interviewee came while I was on a course entitled *From Pork to Chalk— the Effect of Diet on a Child's Brain*. Thus I did not see him and was surprised and delighted when it turned out that the successful candidate was none other than my charming friend John Gribley. He is a visionary and I have always said that to work for him would be a pleasure. Samantha was less convinced initially but I am glad to report that in the last month I have seen a definite thawing in their relationship. It augurs well for the future.

My own teaching goes from strength to strength and I have now introduced what I call 'a communicative approach to language education'. During the majority of my French lessons I indulge the students in rôle playing. There is such liveliness and enthusiasm that the Departmental Head and John Gribley himself have on many occasions looked in to see what was going on. I know they were impressed because recently they have taken to coming in for entire lessons! Even those at the top can learn a thing or two from The Ros! My classroom abuts that of the beautiful Éloise Dublanc who has been a marvellous influence at the school and to whom I feel very close: I often greet her with the words '*Allo Élo!*' She like so many before her finds the Roseman sense of humour a wonderful thing: *Elle est un ouef bon*! My legendary sports coaching has sensibly been used as an example for the less gifted staff and I am now shared out to a different team each day of the week, thereby allowing their respective coaches to sit and absorb at the feet of a Master. Antha continues to market the school although I do not feel this is particularly necessary as we are full.

The children continue to make us both proud and Gribley is always keen to nurture the magnificent brain that sits between Fou Fou Latte's ears. Encouraged by him, she has started a science and inventing club and lately had the British producers of whatever Dolly the Sheep is down to give a talk. FFL is also a leading light in the choir, the netball, swimming and hockey teams, and in the classroom: she is now a year ahead of her peers. In the school production of *The Lion, The Witch and The Wardrobe* she terrorised the young children with her faultless and fearsome portrayal of the White Witch whilst she is a vital cog in the orchestra with her clarinet. Kensington has left Slatterleigh and has made it into St Duke's—what a feather in his cap when one reflects on the struggles he had in early life. He is a weekly boarder and was selected for the football side at the end of term after several members of the team fell ill with food poisoning. We bought him a puppy as a reward for his endeavours and Slippy and Wooflemeister have hit it off. Having a modern marriage, Antha and I share the workload of caring for them; I take them to the golf course (my handicap is now a nifty 31) to exercise them and she feeds, cleans and walks them if it is too wet or cold for golf. In this family I like to feel that we are a real team. Must dash now to see if I can catch Derdle for a pint whilst Antha prepares the supper and puts the children to bed. God bless you all!

Alasdair, Antha, FFL and Kensington

1997

My Christmas letter is, I have often thought, a tonic to friends. Whether through the quality of my literature or the positive tone of my message, I believe that I give people both hope and pleasure. I am therefore sorry to have to begin this particular Round Robin with tragedy. I have spent as much time as I can over the last four months in Kensington Park. I have delivered flowers, left Teddy Bears, read messages and attempted to come to terms with the death of Princess Di. Some of you may not know that I met Diana a few years ago on the touchline of one of Donnington Grove's sports fixtures. We became very close in our five-minute conversation and we knew that we shared the same caring and thoughtful approach to life. And now one of us has gone forever. I cannot understand Antha who consistently refuses to join me on my pilgrimages to West London. It is a blessing that Éloise Dublanc has accompanied me so frequently. Despite the fact that she is French, and must therefore take a great deal of responsibility for Lady Di's death, Éloise has much empathy with me. The outpouring of grief from the British public was perhaps unexpected but it was I—you may recollect—who had been a harbinger★ of this change in attitude when I cried on seeing Johnny Derdle alive last year. I am, I have always maintained, a man ahead of my time.

As one life ends, however, so another begins. On August 31st Samantha gave birth, a full month early, to our third child. She is a little girl who Antha wanted to call Joanna; I, however, decided that she should be called Alasdaira Diana Roseman in honour of the late Princess and my long friendship with her. My watchword is honesty and I have to admit that Alasdaira is not the most attractive of babies; she has flaky skin, a squint and seems to cry all day every day. Until I proposed that Antha and she move downstairs into the sitting room, I managed precious little rest.

★ A sign of things to come; I am a harbinger of a pint for Derdle!

I HAVE ATTEMPTED TO COME TO TERMS WITH THE DEATH OF PRINCESS DI

My sleep patterns have been poor for a few years now and I have been to the doctor several times for check-ups. Indeed, I have had a bad 12 months for health as I have had pharyngitis, a touch of gout, neuralgia in various parts of the body and I suspect that I also have a grumbling appendix. Lucky old Samantha has been in strapping good health although she recently spent a full week in bed with—she said—a fever. She has always been just a little bit precious. Woman 'flu, I'll wager.

We enjoyed a fabulous summer on holiday with Bob and Heather. We had not seen a lot of them in recent times but Bob got in touch and suggested that we join them in their new static caravan on the South Coast. Bob is now nearing 70 but is full of energy and he has lost none of his sharpness at the whist table. He has become an avid twitcher and come rain or high water—and there was a lot of the former on our break—would be out with his binoculars. I frequently accompanied him leaving Antha and Heather to cook and chat about, I assume, pregnancy, knitting and other womanly things. Our two eldest children were, as ever, being looked after by their grandparents who are lucky that we let them see so much of Fouffs and Kensie.

Fouffs has just spent the last term in Quebec on a cultural exchange and, when she returned a couple of days ago, I quizzed her in French about her stay. I am worried that her responses were so unintelligible to me since I am all but fluent. Canadian French is clearly a completely different language. In the earlier part of the year she had dominated prize giving at speech day and was awarded no fewer than eight prizes. I am too modest to boast but she is the cleverest and prettiest girl in the school. Old Gribley looked almost as proud as I when he handed over all the certificates and books to her. Kensie, too, has been abroad this academic year; he travelled to Dijon on an exchange and came back with huge slabs of *stinkingé Brie* and some foul-tasting mustard. His stay was marred by being bitten by a dog which he was attempting to befriend. In the ensuing fight, the wretched creature impaled itself on Kensie's Swiss Army penknife and had to be put down. Poor Kensington has been psychologically damaged by the whole business and the penknife was tragically broken to boot.

Life in Aldworth has been glorious. I hunt down old Derdle in The Bell on most nights and seldom do two evenings pass without my dropping in on him and his good lady wife as they are beginning supper. Once I saw Tucker's car drawing up outside their house and I gave him a terrific surprise by turning up for a drink. I could see he was out of sorts so I insisted on staying on for the meal even though they were all sweetly worried that Antha might have something on the stove for me. I have joined the cricket club and travel with them to all matches even when I am not selected. This is what I call being supportive and I stressed this when Johnny suggested my presence was not necessary. Yesterday I noticed that some joker has put up a For Sale sign outside Johnny's house— probably good old Tucky boy! As I write, Samantha is out watching some ridiculous film about the Titanic (we all know what happens so what is the point?), FFL is reading some tract on philosophy by an unknown author called Potter while looking after Alasdaira, and Kensie is listening to loud music by a passé group called *Hot Chocolate*. Family life! Enjoy Christmas and think kind thoughts.

Alasdair, Antha, Fouffs, Kensie and Alasdaira

1998

On the anniversary of Diana's death, I travelled with Éloise to Paris to look at the infernal underpass where my soul mate passed away. It was an emotional few days, and had the lovely Lois not been there to support me, I do not know how I would have coped. She brought her guitar and we sat in the Jardin du Luxembourg while she played and sung Chris de Burgh hits to me. Were I not already a married man, Éloise would be in with a shout of winning my heart! Rest assured I, like Clinton, did not have sexual relations with that woman! Together we wrote this beautiful song dedicated to the great lady:

Di of flowing hair and of voice cut glass...
Snatched away from me in a foreign underpass
You were my whole life and my whole life was yours—
Your existence was snuffed out on strange shores.
Our splendid lives together were intertwined;
I hope your killer is found, tried and heavily fined.

Touching stuff, *n'es-pa!*

Meanwhile back at home the Wifelet has been becoming a little remiss with her household chores and if Fou Fou Latte did not keep things in order at the weekend, our living conditions would not be acceptable. Consequently I have just employed a married couple—Tony and Tonie Haddock—to work in the garden and house. They are a fiercely ugly pair but, as I remarked to them, 'It doesn't matter what you look like if you can do the work.'

The somewhat feeble reason that the old Trout—I sometimes feel that I have a whole aquarium in my house again—gave for what I can only describe as her sloth is that she has joined the Senior Management Team (SMT) at Slatterleigh Park (SP). It may be 15 or so years since we all said goodbye to Edinburgh but I'm convinced that the majority of you will

I Felt the Part Required a Genuine Thespian.

recall that, although Antha is a pretty little thing of unquestionable pedigree, she is no great thinker. I am surprised, to be frank, that John Gribley looked to her rather than yours truly to join the old think-tank. Given my experience, drive and intellect I would have been a wiser choice. I suspect that in reality, she is no more than eye-candy.

I have, however, been given a new and important job at the school: I have become second assistant director of the Middle School play. We put on *The Wind in the Willows* and the scariness of the weasels and stoats would have been sensational had they remembered their lines rather better. The production was nevertheless a triumph and my portrayal of Toad—I felt the part required a genuine thespian*—was the undoubted highlight. A handful of griping parents felt that I had stolen a child's opportunity, but the play's the thing. Put November 21st in your diaries for next year when, health permitting, I shall be Professor Higgins in *My Fair Lady*!

The theatre has been present in Fou Fou Latte's life as well as she starred as Cosette in *Les Misérables* in the West End for a short spell. She has grown of late and was therefore able to carry off the part despite being too young. Lois, Antha, John and I all went up to see her and, as the reviews suggested, she was wonderful and brought great maturity to the character. It is so amazing that we have both walked the boards with such brilliance in 1998. FFL has been appointed to the School Council and shows off her inimitable skills as an orator when she reports back to the minions at assemblies. Kensington has been flexing his muscles at St Duke's and has had a couple of brushes with authority. He was accused of smoking by his housemaster who stubbornly refused to believe that Kensie had ripped the cigarette out of a friend's hand just as the beak walked in. Our boy abhors smoking and was trying to save his chum from taking the path to nicotine addiction. Do the teachers at these senior schools really understand so little about the characters of those in their charge? The second incident involved the drinking of spirits and K admits to having a swig on a particularly chilly June afternoon—ah there! Boys

* An actor; the word is derived from the Greek island of Thesbos.

will be boys.

Alasdaira has spent almost the entire autumn crying. She is an unhappy little blighter and I was wrong when I thought that her odd looks would pass when she stopped being a tiny baby. She has a screwed up little face and something of a scowl; in many other ways, too, she resembles Antha's mother.

Sadly, Johnny Derdle left the village at the beginning of the year. He made rather a quick sale of his house and departed significantly before what he had told me would be the completion date. I had organised a farewell party which had therefore to be cancelled and Johnny has forgotten to give me a change of address card so I cannot send him a humorous letter of censure! Does anyone have his mobile telephone number? JD's exit left a space on the Parish Council for which both I and Antha were going to stand but I feared that the lassie would be humiliated in the vote and so withdrew my candidature. The generous of spirit have been making sacrifices since the Ark. We celebrate our 15th wedding anniversary next summer and I am looking to do something special with Antha—perhaps it would be appropriate to relive our honeymoon and hook up with Bob and Heather for a week. We may also throw a party and those of you who remember my 30th will be on tenterhooks as you wait for the invitation of the year! Indeed the next 12 months will be busy, as Slatterleigh has an inspection in the spring: the younger teachers are all a quiver but I have promised them the benefit of my wisdom to guide them through the week.

I will be in touch shortly to outline some plans I have to celebrate the end of the millennium but until then we wish you a Merry Christmas and a Happy New Year.

Alasdair, Samantha, Foufflette, Kensie and Alasdaira

1999

Samantha has gone again and this time it is that Judas, John Gribley, who has stolen her. They went to compete in the Thredders Trophy at St Anton—even though neither has lived in Hackthred for some while—and never came back! I am guilty of some exaggeration because they did come back but not to SP; they are holed up in nasty little John's nasty little house near nasty little Bucklebury—with the nasty little Thredders Trophy. Clearly this was a shock for the school and the summer term saw a temporary Head—Ian Slackbotham (and it is!)—struggling at the reins. Once again I was overlooked but I assume this was because the governing body judged sympathetically that I would be too emotionally overwrought to cope. How little they know the strength and depth of The Ros! Slackbotham was all at sea and we staff, the beating heart of the school, waited in trepidation to hear who was to take permanent charge. One evening Éloise and I were sharing a Dubonnet and bitter lemon near the cricket pavilion when—horror of horrors—who should we see the slack one accompanying on a tour of the grounds but GD! Yes, nasty little Graham Davison, Head of the hopeless Donnington Grove, who has all the educational nous of a Minister of Education! The next few weeks were unbearable and I had heart palpitations throughout.

Then, in early July, the new Head was unveiled—GD had fooled the fools. A week later and there I was in a study with him. I presumed he was going to reassure himself that I would not take umbrage at his appointment and would continue to be the very essence of the school. His actual words, which still reverberate around my brain, were 'Roseman, I've never liked you and you are the worst teacher I have ever had the misfortune to meet and the Inspectors agree. Pack your bags and get out!' I retorted—quick as a flash—'Alright but this is a Greyam Dayvison for the school!' I suspect that little quip served as a reminder of just what he was losing—the wittiest and best pedagogue* in the south of England. As

---

* Teacher, not to be confused with paedophile.

It Holds there Within a Future we do not Know.

for those inspectors, they were a frightful bunch who spoke endless jargon about child-centred learning and the like. What have children got to do with good educational practice, I ask you! Anyway, my lawyers will be in touch with the school and GD.

I decided then and there to ask Ellie to leave with me and to seek whatever the winds of fortune might blow our way (why don't I teach English I hear you ask). Éloise kissed me three times on the cheek before replying, '*Non, mon vieus fruit; je rest icee.*' So Roseman was on his own again. It will be no surprise to those who know the extent of my resourcefulness that before a month had gone by I was back in gainful employment grading eggs for a local farmer—none other than the father of all those Stebbington-Brushes. This is no easy job but I quickly mastered it and have found it a restful occupation that has allowed me to compose a charming Ode to an egg:

> *An egg is an oval thing,*
> *Inside it is quite yellow,*
> *It holds there within*
> *A future we do not know.*
> *The world is an egg too—*
> *Except it is not so yellow—*
> *For it holds there within*
> *A future we do not know.*

That little number did not, believe it or not, take me all that long to produce. I may well publish a slim volume of my work in the spring. Do not fret for I have printed a hard copy of the poems in case the millennium bug should destroy all computer files.

Unlike many others I hate both talking and writing about myself, so here is news of the rest of the family. Kensie has his first girlfriend and he has done well for himself as she is none other than the daughter of the Head of St Duke's. She is called Mabel Trenchard and the two are inseparable. I, being an expert on relationships, expect this one to last. Mr Trenchard wrote a rather unfriendly letter demanding that I vouch for my son's behaviour. Having never had any problems with K, I did so by return of post. Kensie is on course to sit eight GCSEs next year and has the genetic pool of my side of the family which should allow him to do very well. Fou Fou Latte is still well ahead of her age group and will sit for GCSEs in 2001. She is studying Spanish now and through a bizarre series of coincidences which I shall not attempt to explain here, she wrote and performed a Spanish love ballad called *Gambas para Mí* which has gone to number two in the charts in Andorra. She is still at SP much to my chagrin but the scholarship is too valuable to be abandoned—I have my principles. I had hoped that Alasdaira would go and live with her mother but Samantha did not want her and so she is being looked after during the day by the Haddocks—my employees. This is probably no bad thing as Alasdaira may thereby come to believe that she is not that ugly after all. I gather that she has begun to put a few short sentences together and she waddles towards me in an uncoordinated fashion in the evenings and wails.

I don't know how you will all be spending the New Year but my children will be with their mother along with Slippy the dog. Wooflemeister and I shall be heading off to spend the night with Heather and Bob, who recently was the unfortunate victim of a stroke.

Alasdair, Fouffs, Kensie and Alasdaira

2000

I trust that the new millennium finds you all in fighting form. This is going to be my era, of that much I am confident. I have, in general, been gainfully employed ever since I called a halt to my teaching career in 1999. I had been at the cutting edge of education for almost all my working life and had proved to myself and the world that here was a natural Schoolmaster. Graham Davison, it is perfectly obvious, had always felt threatened by my greater ability and used the Inspectors' lack of vision as an excuse to lever me out of Slatterleigh. But it is an ill wind… I shall not return to the classroom ever and if anyone sees me heading in that direction, they have my permission to shoot me (God bless Steve Redgrave). Having shown myself to be a great Egg Grader of the highest calibre, I moved into the thrilling and challenging world of the concrete factory. Bracknell is a long commute but it is at the hub of the modern world and I love getting my hands dirty. Mixing concrete is an art form and it takes an artist such as I to create beautiful blocks. I have seldom been happier and I see myself working here for the foreseeable future. I have, in my spare time, moulded some concrete cows *à la Milton Keynes*★ and they now reside in the garden unworried by the advance of Mad Cow Disease, unlike my mother-in-law (lol!).

I have been suffering from serious fatigue for months now and have taken to my bed on several occasions. The doctor has prescribed me some pills and has referred to 'The Black Dog' as being at the root of my weariness. This shows how little he knows, for Wooflemeister was a glorious gold and kept me cheerful throughout his tragically short life. Yes, Wooflemeister is no more: he died unexpectedly last month. We think that he ate something that did not agree with him. Poor Kensie was distraught as he had only just recovered from the shock of being expelled from St Duke's. It was alleged—the evidence seemed totally spurious to me—that he had poisoned the school dog. Slippy, our other dog, has sunk into a

★ This new town was named after the great economist John Milton Keynes.

depression
out of which he
really must shake himself. We cannot
let the slings and arrows of outrageous fortune mess us up. It was a sad end
to K's career at St Duke's as he had excelled in his GCSEs in which he
secured five passes which is above the national average by a stretch. He
will resit Mathematics, Science and English once we find a school that
will take him. Do bear in mind that the poor boy was not even 15 when
he sat the examinations. At present, Kensie is very sensibly keeping his
academic interests alive in the garden shed. He explained to me that he is
doing a variety of experiments which involve, as far as I can see and smell,
a lot of smoke. I hope he is not working too hard for he often emerges
from this den in something of a daze.

Fou Fou Latte is developing into a startlingly attractive young lady and
has decided to stay at Slatterleigh rather than move to an all-girls' school.
She has been seen on the arm of a variety of hideous and acnoid youths,
none of whom is good enough for her. She has started a radio station at
the local hospital, which she has taken to visiting several times a week. She
presents her own music show and also runs a weekly discussion

This is Going To Be My Millennium

programme entitled *The Philosophers' Club*. It is exceptionally difficult to follow the logic of its contributors' arguments even for one as switched on as myself. I nearly forgot to mention that Fouffs has taken one GCSE (she was still 12 at the time) and managed an A* in French. Her academic career seems destined to follow the same trajectory as mine.

For those of you who wish for word of that Jezebel, Samantha, I can report that she is still shacked up with Grubby Gribley in Bucklebury. She is vehement in her demands that FFL spend alternate weekends with her but does not pull her weight with the slug-like Alasdaira—and one has to pull one's weight since Alasdaira has considerable weight of her own. I need time away from the mewling infant so that I can compose more of my poems. The hideous Haddocks are proving loyal staff and do some babysitting but I have a suspicion that they find my youngest child as vexing as I do. FFL appears to have some patience with the girl and that at least keeps her away from me for much of the time. I had word from Norman Jones in September; he has been living in Sweden for some time and has been involved in the film industry there, I gather. He is intending to return to Blighty shortly.

As planned, I saw the new millennium in with Bob and Heather and I was glad that I did so for Bob passed away a few brief weeks later. The funeral was a sad affair with just a handful of mourners. How tragic to have so few friends. A week after that, I celebrated my 40th birthday in a Frankie and Benny's restaurant with the children and the Haddocks. It was a splendid affair with the waiters assembling around our table to sing happy birthday and then old Cliff belting out *Congratulations* on a CD! An unforgettable night with sparklers all round! One final piece of news to round off what has been a terrific year for us: Éloise Dublanc sent me an early Christmas card—I think she still has a soft spot for me. Season's Greetings to you all!

Alasdair, Fou Fou Latte, Kensington and Alasdaira (I suppose.)

2001

It has generally been a wonderful year for the Rosemans and indeed it has been a wonderful year for the world if you forget the little contretemps of the twin towers. The latter event and terrorism in general had a knock-on effect for me as I received a letter from an unknown source and shortly afterwards began to feel poorly. I had a sore throat, a mild fever and my muscles ached—it was, I feared, likely to be anthrax. I sped my way to the John Radcliffe Hospital where I had to wait an inordinate time before seeing a doctor. It was the same quack who diagnosed my suspected heart attack of a few years ago as a pulled muscle across the chest. (I have never mentioned the coronary to anyone before as I hate to alarm friends.) The fellow did not really have a clue and said that it was 'flu and sent me away. You can imagine my thoughts as I lay in bed awaiting death. A lesser man would have been quaking but I faced my impending demise with equanimity for I have enjoyed a rich life. Anthrax is usually a killer but I have now shown that those of us imbued with great mental fortitude can survive it for, within 24 hours, I was up and about. Sometimes I surprise even myself. There is a message in these traumatic events for each and every one of us: terrorism will change all our lives. You may be luckier than I was, but be alert.

The spring saw romance in the air for both Kensington and me. His girlfriend and he went on holiday to Florida where they paid a visit to Mr Michael Mouse. They spent a fortnight on their own doing the whole Disney, Seaworld and Universal Studios caboodle★. Mabel is a couple of years older than my boy but was glad of his courage, I gather, as they faced the horror of three-hour queues at the Epcot centre. They obviously ate like Americans for K returned home a right porker—I could see that he is Alasdaira's brother. Meanwhile Éloise Dublanc came like a ray of garlic-smelling sunshine into my life. She had remained ensconced in Slatterleigh Park after my resignation but arrived one evening at my door announcing that she missed me terribly and thought that she had 'feelings' for me. *'Bon sûr,'* I replied, *'Apres tout tu est une faim!'* Within a month she and I were living together and when she retired at the end of the summer term, she was already out of her school accommodation and thus did not have to deal with the double whammy of turning 60 and finding a new house at the same time. We are very happy and of an evening I will work on my stamp collection while Ellie pursues her bizarre hobby of reading Estate Agency literature. The only glimmer of a problem on the horizon is that I have had a series of telephone calls from the old Trout who does not seem terribly happy with gruesome Gribley. His new business venture does not seem to be going well but I told Samantha to hang on in there and that I was filing for divorce.

Business ventures bring me on to the subject of work. In May, Normy returned to the country like the prodigal son and I, who have never had other than the greatest of respect for the man, slaughtered the fatted calf and took him out to a Chinese in Bracknell. Over the noodles we hit upon a quite splendid and original business plan. We would set up a tutorial company at Aldworth with Norm teaching music and I giving lessons in French, Mathematics—yes I can do that too—Latin and Physics. We called it 'NormAl Services' and advertised in all the local papers and once we had two clients, I abandoned my budding concrete career. But within a month, another player had entered the market for my services—

★ The whole lot; the poorly-educated will say 'the whole caboodle', resulting in what we grammarians call a tautology.

ÉLOISE DUBLANC CAME LIKE A RAY OF GARLIC-SMELLING SUNSHINE.

Merethrop Manor. Yes, that is right, the fine preparatory school near Goring whose fortunes have waned of late. They were seeking a French and Latin teacher for September and snapped up the chance of employing me, given my extensive experience. (Latin will be an entirely new department and one that will flourish under my stewardship!) Michael Millicent and Norman wrote the appropriate glowing references for me and I was in. Maybe some time in the future 'NormAl Services' will be resumed. Needless to say, I slipped seamlessly back into a way of life which is as much as part of me as Fou Fou Latte. I make it a rule never to bore people in my Christmas letter but forgive me this once for revealing that I shall be in charge of the 1st XI football. I think I will play a 4-4-2 system with one of the centre backs dropping deep. Maybe I'll drop a line to this Sven Goran Eriksson fellow and we can compare notes. Norman has taught FFL a little Swedish and can help her pen the letter.

Ah, Fouffs! What a girl! She has been busy gaining another 14 A*s at GCSE in what I like to call strong subjects, not like old Kensie. She has begun her 'A' level courses and is two, if not three, years ahead of where she should be. She is writing poetry (a chip off the old block), running her radio station, ensuring that the Haddocks do their jobs properly, caring for Fat Al—as I call Alasdaira—doing some modelling and regularly singing in concerts. It is no wonder that she now only occasionally boards! I know that the girl would prefer to be with her father all the time but she sacrifices her wishes on the altar of Samantha's demands. I trust this missive arrives in time for the 25th; I was so excited at the prospect of seeing *The Fellowship of the Ring* that I almost forgot to write the thing. There is a fancy dress party at The Bell tonight and I am going as a Bilbo! Life cannot get much better.

Alasdair, Éloise, FFL, K and Fat Al

2002

I am glad that Christmas has arrived again for it gives me the chance to set the record straight with those of you whom I have not seen in the last year. In September it was widely reported in the national press that Merethrop Manor had lost a boy in a cave whilst on an outward bound holiday. One scurrilous newspaper even named me as the teacher in charge. Its front page headline—'In a cave? Cave★ Roseman!'—was particularly cruel, even though I had to admit to a degree of admiration for the classicist who must have penned it.

It is true that I travelled with the school to Buckfastleigh to indulge in some potholing and it is equally true that one pupil was temporarily mislaid—a lad called Giles Brushington-Stebb. However, the responsibility must lie with the foolish 10-year-old child (let me name no names, Tim Tallow) who, at the end of our two-hour session, told me that we were all back above ground. We returned in the minibus to our accommodation and it was actually only my professionalism that saved the day; the next morning I was about to help myself to the croissant that was left over when I registered that one croissant too many, meant one child too few! Within a couple of hours, after having finished breakfast, we were back at the top of the vertical ladder that descended into the Stygian gloom. Giles was sitting a mere 100 yards into the cave complex and I gave him a third of the croissant that I had saved for him—the rest I had already devoured, as worry makes me suffer painful pangs of hunger. Personally I suspect that the whole experience will have done the fellow a great deal of good; today's children are desperately soft. Our Headmaster did have words with me and there the matter would have ended, had Tim Tallow not contacted the Fourth Estate. Incidentally the photograph of me that the papers all used made me look absurdly old but the press are notoriously 'Cave-alier' (!) with accuracy.

Back at school I have been on sensational form in all areas of my job.

★ Beware; similar to the motto of agoraphobics—*Caveat emptor.*

IN A CAVE?

'Cave' Roseman

EYE WITNESS REPORT—TIM TALLOW

kenen onenenn onenni eneenen onn
penenn onenni konn onenen nenen onen onn
nenenenennn on onennenn.

nenen onenenni onenen on onenna onn
onenenenn onn onenn onenen onena onenn
onenenenn onenenen onenn onenn

ROSEMAN (42)

onenenenn onenn
enenennenn
nenenenennn
enenenn onenn
nenenenn

MISLAID

nenen onen onenn
onenennen onenni
nenenenn
onenenenenn
nenenenenenn
onenennen onenni
nenenonennn

PUBLIC INQUIRY?

nenenenenen onn
onenenenennn on
nenenenn

nenennnenenn
nenenenennnn
onenenenennn
onenenenn
onenenenenn
onenenenenn
onenenenn
nenenn onenn onn
onenenenennn.

BRUSHINGTON-STEBB (10)

The French results saw several children secure 'A' grades including the Gréville twins—André and Camille—and Julien Pétillant. Latin scores at Merethrop have never been better and the school play, *The Thwarting of Baron Bolligrew* in which I performed as the eponymous hero, was a triumph according to the school magazine: 'Mr Roseman showed that he could have made a career on the stage.' I have also extended my contributions to daily life by editing that august journal. Most notable of my achievements, however, has been the coaching of an unbeaten 1st XI football side! What a season we enjoyed. I was also able to pass on my wisdom to my assistant, Marcus Stebbington-Brush, whom I used to teach, and who has joined the staff after completing a postgraduate course at Cambridge where, my sources tell me, he managed to get a Blue in soccer. So you can see that my career is burgeoning and that I may yet decide to become a Headmaster.

My private life has been equally fulfilling for I am now—at 42—a proud grandfather. Kensington elected not to return to school after his excellent GCSEs. He and Mabel had a child in July and are now living in a council house outside Reading. Kensie would love to be working but has rightly taken the view that a father's place is with his child. Little Kyle is lucky indeed to have such a caring parent. Mabel, after an extensive period of recuperation during which, I'm afraid to say, her figure did not really return, has begun training as a nurse.

Fou Fou Latte has, if this is possible for one so brilliant, surpassed herself by achieving four A grades at 'A' Level in one year. She did all the necessary modules in half the normal time and was awarded a scholarship to Trinity, Oxford where she is reading PPE. I am delighted as that very same college had interviewed me back in 1978 and would have offered me a place, had I not elected to head north of the border. Fouffs chose not to take a 'Gap' year after my paternal lecture about 'not getting behind.' She comes home frequently to relieve the Haddocks from the chore of looking after Fat Al, who continues to disappoint. It would be fair to say that she is the forgotten child and one that I do not like. She has developed an unfortunate skin disease and her speech is embarrassingly far behind the level that FFL had reached at her age. We can only hope that she does not become a blight on all our lives. I recently penned a little ditty about her that will make you all laugh:

> *When God made Alasdaira,*
> *On looks he chose to spare 'er.*
> *No man will want to snare 'er,*
> *'Cos she's a right pig-scarer!*

I have framed it and hung it in her room in the hope that her father making her The Muse of his verse will make her feel special.

In March I decided that the life that Éloise Dublanc and I were leading together was not satisfactory and I asked her to *'Departez de mon vie.'* To put it kindly—and I did—she is old and boring. She took it bravely, remarkably so in fact, and was soon living in a cottage in Blewbury. The old Trout seems to have patched up her differences with Gribley and they have moved to Pangbourne. I have decided that I am too big a man to harbour grudges and sporadically drop in for supper with them. They are doubtless grateful for some intellectual company and I even suggested that I join their Book Club but I withdrew the offer when I heard that they were about to read *Atonement* by Ian McEwan. He writes well enough—and I should, you will agree, know—but a bit of a detective story is more my kind of thing. Norman Jones was keen to renew our erstwhile tenant-landlord relationship but I have other fish to fry. I am too tactful to divulge any more but there is a sweet little maid in the French department at school on whom Alasdair 'The Spider' Roseman has cast his web.

Have a wonderful Christmas—I shall unfortunately not, as sister Charmaine is coming to stay.

Alasdair and Fou Fou Latte

2003

Blessed are those who have their health! Despite my reluctance to succumb to illness and notwithstanding my fighting spirit, I have had to be off work for some of the year. I was struck down by a February bug and was unable to be in school for a full fortnight. This was desperately unfortunate for both me and the school as I was consequently forced to miss the Inspection. My French teaching is the stuff of legend and I have single-handedly put Merethrop Classics on the map. The Inspectors were denied a thrilling experience. I phoned the Head at the start of the week in question and iterated my intention to come in 'for school and country.' He would not hear of it and told me that he and my colleagues would try to battle through alone. It is fortunate that my influence on the departments in which I work is so strong for the reports that they received were positively glowing. How refreshing to have these bureaucrats acknowledging that I am a teacher of the highest order. The summer term saw me sickening again and for the pupils this could have been disastrous as I was away for a month before their examinations. It is a further tribute to my skill as a teacher that I had already covered enough ground with them to enable their results to be infinitely improved on those of the students of 2002. I am justly proud of my charges and myself.

I subtly hinted in last year's letter that romance was in the air and indeed the fly that 'The Spider' was stalking has been ensnared in my web! I am to Melissa Tidewell what Shelob was to Frodo Baggins. Melissa is, as I mentioned, in the French department and is just 25. She is stunning looking—a former model—and has been enthralled by my worldliness, charm and disarming modesty. I have worked in all the major spheres of life whether it be industry, finance, publishing/books and of course education and, for a young girl like Melissa, I must be an awe-inspiring figure. I wined and dined her at many of the excellent hostelries of the Thames Valley and in May the deal was done: she moved into Aldworth.

Too Large to Fit into the Box.

She has much to learn in the way of cooking (I seem to have a knack of picking the duff ones in that department) but we have nonetheless been entertaining local friends with a series of dinner parties. There is now a sense of desperation in the pub amongst those who have yet to be called to our high table. I have always considered myself to be a popular fellow but my urbane and wise company is, I'll wager, making our invitation the most sought after in the south of England.

We are planning to have children of our own but may have to wait until I can find a boarding school that will take Alasdaira for I do not want her to spoil our family life. Alasdaira is only six and all the establishments that I have approached have been most unhelpful and refuse to take her until she turns eight. Being a splendid father to Fat Al, whom I now also humorously refer to as The Buddha, I organised a birthday party for her on the 31st August. I made a short speech to the little guests reminding them that the date was only really special because a great lady had died on it and then touched on the memorable moments of Diana's life. Fifteen minutes later it was time for Marvo the Magician to chop Alasdaira in half. Sadly, The Buddha was too large to fit into the box and so her friend Magnus was put under the knife. I cannot believe that Alasdaira has so many friends (she possibly bribed them to attend) but there were 24 of them and the party was expensive. How lucky that my parents both died this year since it allows us to afford such occasions, as well as the opportunity to pack Fat Al off to a boarding school as soon as possible.

My parents' joint funeral was a thoroughly enjoyable affair as so many of you emerged out of the woodwork. For the few of you who wrote to say you could not attend, let me tell you that Tucker and Johnny were both there and Flic Tamworth came with Lorna, Zöe and Olivia. Nicola dragged along Bert, and John came with Catherine; there were 450 people in the church! I never understood why people liked the old folks so much and to be candid I had nothing in common with them. Charmaine's eulogy* was, I'm sure everybody agreed, a cloying and

---

* Speech of praise: farmers who talk in glowing terms about their sheep are delivering a 'ewelogy'; those of you who praise my Christmas letters are giving me a 'Yulogy'!

tedious speech; who wanted to hear those anecdotes about Pa's heroics in the war or Ma's endless good deeds in the community? She might at least have mentioned me more than once but that has always been Charmaine's problem; she can't see beyond her own sad little life. I apologise for the fact that you were denied the pleasure of hearing The Ros at the pulpit, but with a fair wind you will listen to my pearls at a wedding in the not too distant future!

Shortly after the funeral, John and Samantha tied the knot. Their wedding was a tacky affair at which the only worthwhile thing was the oration of Fou Fou Latte. She was splendid and showed just why she has become such a leading light of the Oxford Union. She has been involving herself in university life to the full—just like her dad, eh!—and rowed in the victorious crew at the boat race at Henley. She was Desdemona in a wonderful production of *Othello* and has been earning money in a series of advertisements. She has rediscovered a childhood talent for Art and accepted my commission to sculpt a bust of myself. It is devastatingly handsome; the resemblance is quite uncanny. She spends a lot of time here with Fat Al and even finds time to chat to the Haddocks who had quite a nasty smash in their car in April, rendering them 'battered haddocks'! Luckily they haven't had their chips!

Slippy the dog is always pleased to see Fou Fou as she, unlike me, has the time to walk him. She then pops along to Blewbury to see Kyle and Mabel and to try to find out if there is any word of Kensington who has temporarily disappeared. The poor fellow has some of his mother's less charming genes.

I'm so pleased to have so many of your new addresses—another advantage of parental death! Merry Christmas but not, I have just heard, for Saddam: 'We got him'!

Alasdair, Melissa, FFL and The Buddha(!)

WE SET OUT ON OUR HONEYMOON.

2004

On April 1st, wedding bells chimed out for The Ros and his beautiful bride Melissa Tidewell—except they didn't, as we preferred to marry quietly in a Registry Office in Didcot. Melissa was keen to have an extravagant celebration in her family church near Wootton Bassett, envisaging a marquee in her parents' enormous garden and a huge party on the evening of the great day. I said no. What with my vast network of friends and the odd chum of hers, there simply wouldn't have been room in the church or indeed in the tent. So, I argued with my typical cogency, it would be better not to cause jealousy by disappointing some and not others. A fairer solution could be achieved quite simply by disappointing everyone.

I also pointed out to Liss that it would be pretty selfish of me to have a second society wedding when some unfortunates could not even afford one. Thus it was just family—minus Kensington—and the Haddocks (Mr was my Best Man) who gathered in unpretentious Didcot for our big day. We all had lunch in a lovely Pizza restaurant in Abingdon and then as man and wife we set out on our honeymoon. My parents had left their cottage on Loch Awe in Scotland to me and Charmaine—it is such a romantic spot that I thought we should go there. To keep it as a surprise for Liss, I had told her to pack sun tan lotion and to make sure she had plenty of dollars. So you can imagine her reaction when we climbed on a plane bound for Glasgow! The head of the Loch has a reputation for being one of the wettest spots in the United Kingdom but it was barely spitting when our hired Smart Car reached the foot of Ben Cruachan. We stocked up with provisions at the local Spar and then returned down the eastern side of the loch. It was a bLISSful week, with Melissa able to get some cooking practice whilst I shared a dram or seven with Billy Stewart who looks after the cottage for us. It was a particular joy when Billy brought out his bagpipes on the third night. I insisted on a reprise every day after that.

It was quite a jolt to return to school for the summer term, I can tell you. But, ever the old pro, I quickly adapted to it and indeed to yet another new position. It had been decided that the best use of my talents would be for me to give all classes one lesson of oral French and one gripping period on Greek and Roman myths each week. This meant that nobody would be denied the privilege of my tuition. I have heard that many parents ask nervously whether their offspring will be taught by Mr Roseman. The myths allowed me to display a myriad of virtuoso performances whether playing Jason as he slew the Minotaur or Medusa as he vainly fought off the unwanted attentions of Hercules. My oral lessons have been an absolute triumph and consequently the school's French results have improved once more.

On the sports field, the 1st XI soccer again conquered all, although Marcus Stebbington-Brush is becoming a trifle uppity and should remember that I am older, wiser and taller than he. Had we adopted the 2-3-5 formation we would have won our matches in much more attractive fashion. My only concern about Merethrop is that they have a rather callow bunch on the SMT. I have offered my services on several occasions but the Head contends that he cannot risk damaging my 'extraordinary contributions' in other walks of school life, which is, I suppose, the truth of the matter.

Fou Fou Latte has had a relatively quiet year by her standards and her highlight must have been coxing the Oxford men's eight to victory on the long haul from Putney to Mortlake. She has also unfortunately been guilty—for the first time in her life—of wasting her talents. She is working for a charity which helps the homeless, when she should be concentrating on her degree. These people should, to coin an old phrase, 'get on their bikes and find some work' and, while they are at it, a house. FFL will not listen to her old man, however, and I fear that she will pay a heavy price some time in the future. Her examination results this year were outstanding.

Fouffs has also been spending time tracking down her errant brother, who has been located in the Democratic Republic of Congo★, where he has been looking after the war veterans. FFL flew out to see him and reported that he had a series of scars where stray bullets had hit him and that he seemed somewhat jumpy. I hope that he will return home as Mabel and Kyle miss him. Mabel's loneliness has been lessened by the arrival of Normy Jones in her house. Normy is now a peripatetic music teacher and loves coming home to company and good food of which, Mabel tells me, he often has a lot on his plate. Alasdaira, who is at Merethrop, continues to disappoint and I sense that she does not value me as much as she should. She and her coterie of foolish friends run around the buildings as if without a care in the world, always laughing and chatting. They should settle down to some serious graft—perhaps it is The Buddha who has been setting Fou Fou Latte a bad example.

Next year it is my 45th birthday and I am having another bash! The invitations are enclosed with this letter—I will see you all there. Happy Christmas—God bless us, every one!

Alasdair, Liss, Fou Fou Latte, Kensie (in absentia),
The Buddha and Slippy the Dog

★ Formerly Ceylon—the African Studies element of my degree is frequently useful.

THE BARBECUE TO END ALL BARBECUES.

2005

It is difficult to believe that ten months have passed since my 45th birthday party was celebrated in such style! Many of you were there in February as the barbecue to end all barbecues took place. It is a peculiarly masculine trait to be able to manage the flames coming off the charcoal and one with which I have not struggled in the past. The inquest concluded that in a moment when I was temporarily indisposed, a turkey twizzler caught light just as a gust of wind caused a curtain to blow onto it. The rest, as they say, is history.

Two things occurred to me as I surveyed the ruins of our sitting room: firstly, Jamie Oliver is right that twizzlers are dangerous; secondly the intimacy of an indoor barbecue may not be sufficient cause to hold one. The fire brigade did a decent job in saving most of the house but some of their remarks towards me were downright impolite. The world is changing and not, I would say, for the better. It was particularly nice, however, to welcome to the festivities Tucker—my first Best Man—my first wife and John Gribley.

The most amusing upshot of the hooley was revealed in May, when Samantha dumped John for Tucker! Antha had persuaded Tucker to come along, although presumably she had not had to work too hard as he must have been keen as mustard to see his mucker, The Ros. He always had a soft spot for the old Trout at university but had lost out to the better man and was now content to pick up the scraps from off my plate. As for Gribley, the truth is out about him: he is the sort of man for whom I feel deep pity; the sort of man who cannot hold on to his woman. I occasionally stroll along to see him in Pangbourne so that I can give him sage advice but he appears to be but a broken reed. Samantha and Simon, as she insists on calling him, have meanwhile moved to Wales, so not everything is going swimmingly for them either. Maybe they will eventually walk down the aisle but I'll (note that my punning is still top notch) be surprised.

Fou Fou Latte graduated this year with a First—I never doubted her application and ability for one moment. Oxford will be a poorer place without her and they begged her to stay to do a PhD but she very properly felt that she could not afford the time. While studying, she wrote and had published her first novel *The Wretchedness of Iniscara Denis,* which you may have seen was one of Richard and Judy's summer reads. I can thoroughly recommend a brief perusal; it tells the tale of a very young girl who is cruelly neglected by her father but, having taken solace in food, finds a better solution by using her charisma★ to form a tight network of friendships which eventually enable her to triumph against the odds. I found the subject matter improbable and thought that Fou Fou allowed some of her sentences to drag on when with the careful use of punctuation she could have shortened them without dramatically altering the punch that the book undeniably has from its first page to the last. FFL then organised the charity walk that was a major part of our summer holidays. The walk was for the homeless and we all joined her with the exception of Alasdaira. Although my youngest has lost a fair amount of weight, I thought that her presence might spoil the atmosphere. She was left with the Haddocks but, I was furious to discover, spent the entire fortnight with friends.

FFL, Kensie (yes, he's back!), Mabel and Kyle, Melissa, Slippy the dog and I all gathered in St Bees to tackle the Coast to Coast path made famous by Wainwright. The weather was glorious as the magnificent seven strode towards the Lake District, even if some of the others moved with an awkward gait. Five miles in and I fell off the top of an awkward gate (!) and sustained a suspected fracture of my ankle. I have a high threshold of pain but had to bow to the excruciating torture and was picked up by the van of Coast-to-Coast Packhorse. The others continued for 12 days at what I considered to be a lamentable pace, whilst I became a tourist. Some of the accents up north are a tad uncultured and to make myself understood, I had to speak loudly and forcefully. That is the way to deal

---

★ The magnetism of character that everybody agrees I have. No comment! (But I know they are right.)

with these people. On the last day, I joined the trekkers again for our final assault on Robin Hood's Bay. My injury was still causing me significant distress but I kept this hidden. How proud we all felt as we walked down the hill to the North Sea having completed 192 miles—that is an achievement that would be beyond many. I confess that I did sprint the final 200 yards so that I was the first to complete the walk. It is hard to take the competitive edge out of the true sportsman. We succeeded in raising £25,000 and this would have been considerably more had I had opportunity in my busy summer term to contact one or two sponsors. My real gift to the team was my motivational genius that kept us going when

some were wilting and moaning about sore feet—psychosomatic if you ask me. It was a sadness that Kensie was unable to save Slippy from falling under the wheels of a car as they were crossing the A6136, having fallen behind the rest of the walking party.

Kensington returned from Africa in March and has moved back in with Mabel, Kyle and Normy. He prefers not to talk about his time in the war but apparently his sleep patterns are unsettled and he often talks while slumbering with the line 'Take that!' most frequently repeated. I have tried to persuade him to relax by joining me in the score hut at Aldworth's cricket fixtures but he is not convinced that this will help him. Anyway, to finish on another cricketing note: well done to Vaughan, Freddie and the boys—they reminded me of my own cricketing career when it was at its peak. Festive greetings to you all!

Alasdair, Melissa, Fouffs, Kensington and Alasdaira

I HAVE BECOME A MAINSTAY OF THE GROUNDSTAFF TEAM.

2006

I am a man of great moral stature as you, my many friends, appreciate and I worry about the way the world is going. I have always been a forward thinker and there is nothing of the Luddite in me. Even so, I cannot but help fear for the future of our educational system when those as gifted as me find themselves sidelined by Modernist thinking. Merethrop is my spiritual home—I am Merethrop and Merethrop is me. Where Merethrop ends and I begin cannot be seen. I even call myself Mr Merethrop. I can honestly and in all modesty state that I stand for all that is best at Merethrop. So when the Head announced—without consultation—that my mythology lessons were to be replaced by something called 'Citizenship', I raged like Narcissus. The very next week I heard that my French Oral lessons were to be scrapped in order to create room in the curriculum for 'Circle time'. *Ben, dit—don:* I cannot believe that the Mathematics department really require yet another lesson to be devoted to π D and all that malarkey★.

As the September term dawned, a third dagger was plunged into my teaching soul: the sports staff believed that my considerable knowledge would be best exploited if I were merely to referee fixtures and training games. I have since proved that I am indeed a first class arbiter but, given my extraordinary success with the 1st XI, it had to be a foolish decision. I am glad to say that my legacy to the team was sufficient to enable them to enjoy another unbeaten season last term, even though I was no longer at the helm. Marcus Stebbington-Brush did not seem to realise the enormous debt that he owes me—such is the ingratitude of youth. My importance to the school remains undiminished as, apart from blowing the whistle, I have become a mainstay of the groundstaff team. I have indeed written a poem about life on the tractor which it would be cruel not to share with you:

★ Whole caboodle.

I cut and mow and mow and cut.
I scatter and strew and strew and scatter.
To nature my mind is open not shut;
It is the beasts and plants that really matter.

Beautiful and succinct you will concur.

This year has, blessedly, not been without its joys and chief amongst these was the birth in late May of twin sons to Melissa and me. We have given them the distinguished names of Marmaduke and Eric and they are a chortling pair of lads. Their birth was a dramatic affair. Liss and I had hired a rowing boat from Abingdon and Liss was pulling away at the oars as we passed by Radley. Ten minutes later and she began to gripe about some pains. I told her to mind her malingering and remember that she was Fou Fou Latte's stepmother and that rowing was therefore in her blood. Nevertheless a further five minutes up the river she ploughed the vessel through some weeping willows (I was quite badly scratched) and onto a mudbank on the shore. There, a few contractions took place and then out popped the boys: easy! They were a day before their due date and I had only got a penknife to cut the umbilical cords. I duly handed it to Melissa who did the deed. The Haddocks have proved excellent nannies and take the boys and Melissa home with them in the evenings so that my sleep need not be disturbed.

My elder children have had an interesting year too. Fou Fou Latte flew out to Sri Lanka immediately after Boxing Day last year to help the victims of the Tsunami. I tried to explain to her that she needed to look after her own interests and that somebody else could earn God's gratitude—probably someone Irish. FFL can be stubborn and she wasted six months out there when she could have been finding a job. She was 18 by then, and not getting any younger, and quite apart from that she had to live in rudimentary accommodation. I sometimes wonder just how bright my Fouffs is. Fortunately, when she returned she went to a series of interviews with City firms and is now employed by Goldman Sachs and living in Fulham.

Kensington has made his own mistakes too; in the height of the summer his house in Blewbury was raided and he and Norman were arrested (!) for conducting dog fights. I cannot credit this as Kensie has always cared for and nurtured his pets. How he loved Wooflemeister, Slippy, Perkins, Ange, Gel and Fish, Fluffy, Bunnykins and the rest! He spent the night in prison and when the case came to court he was heavily fined, notwithstanding my splendid character reference. Norm was given a warning only, as he had agreed to testify against K. Rather harshly and, lacking his customary Christian spirit, Kensington then threw Normy out of the house and so my friend is once more lodged with me. And Alasdaira? She has—like Pluto—had to be downgraded. Pluto is now a mere dwarf planet and Alasdaira is no longer a Buddha. The correction of her squint was paid for by the parents of a friend of hers which I personally disapproved of but Samantha gave the go-ahead. My belief is that you should stick with the cards you are dealt at birth. She spends week upon week with the incredibly long-suffering families of a variety of her chums.

I have not heard much news of old acquaintances and friends this year but I do gather that old Johnny Derdle became the Tory M.P. for Henley at the election last year. This could prove a frightfully good jape as I have some interesting university photographs of him. I know he has a terrific sense of humour and he might like to see his picture plastered all over the front pages of the tabloids. Watch that space! Well, the twins, Melissa and the Haddocks have just left for the night, so I'm heading to Pangbourne to cheer up Gribley. Enjoy your winterval.

Alasdair, Liss, The Buddha that was, Normy and the twins

2007

Contrary to reports that you may have heard I am in fine health—just a trace of gout, high levels of cholesterol, a weak chest and some unexplained dizziness—but it cannot be denied that this has been a difficult year and one that would have sunk ships less seaworthy than me. Let me tell everyone the way things stand so that foul rumour may not distort the truth. As the winter was breathing its last, I travelled, as has been my wont these past few months, to Pangbourne to drop in on John Gribley. It was a working day but I had finished sweeping the Merethrop schoolyard and decided to pay one of my oldest, and I thought, truest friends a visit. I let myself in through his back door and, finding no one downstairs, I climbed the staircase and there, in his singularly unpleasant open-plan bedroom, I saw a terrible sight. This is a Christmas letter so suffice it to say that I beheld John, Melissa and Normy in a *manege à trois*. To be honest, I had not known that the three had ever met so I was perplexed. I remained controlled: 'Hello,' I said, 'Would anyone like a cup of tea?' With that I spun round—unfortunately stumbling and twisting my ankle in so doing—and stalked out with my head held high and dignity intact.

The upshot of this has been that I have left the family seat at Aldworth, have left Merethrop Manor and am now living in leafy Lilyville Road in Fulham in Fou Fou Latte's spare bedroom. How painful it was to depart from a job that I had loved! The Head made a splendid speech at the end of the Easter term in which he congratulated Henry Hertzel on his scholarship to Harrow (a bit of an oxymoron those last three words) and wished Alan Roseman well in 'whatever the future holds for him.' He has always called me Alan and I shall treasure the copy of *Cooking for Single Men* that the staff signed and presented to me as a mark of their esteem.

Back in Berkshire, the sinful three have set up house together in my cottage and are bringing up Marmy and Eric in a den of iniquity*.

★ Wickedness. Terrible wickedness. Unacceptable wickedness.

I Love Being a Man About Town

I would rescue them if it were possible but am biding my time. The sinners are welcome to Alasdaira. She has somehow conned the examining body of Headington School and has been awarded a Sports' Scholarship and a Bursary. I am led to believe by Gribley, with whom I chat on the phone from time to time, that she is the star of her year. I somehow doubt it and conjecture that this is all part of Gribley's Walter Mitty existence. The fellow needs to take a grip.

Life in London has been thrilling and I love being a man about town. I am taking full advantage of living in the capital. I walk in South Park, visit the Fulham Broadway cinema and use an Oyster Card. I am on the verge of contacting my many London friends and imagine that, once everybody digests the fact that The Ros is back in circulation, I will be greatly sought after on the dinner party circuit. So, you London lot, I await your calls. I am not going to rush into any teaching post and am perusing the TES at my leisure for a suitable position for one of my seniority. In the interim I earn an honest crust by distributing Estate Agent leaflets for Charmaine's company. There is something hugely therapeutic about walking the length of a street popping paper through the letterboxes and it has allowed me time to compose more poetry. Once again I give you a Christmas taste of my work:

> *London existence is a fine life,*
> *Denied the country by my wife.*
> *I drift around its famous parks*
> *Listening to the music of the larks.*
> *My thoughts are so remarkably deep*
> *If you heard them you would weep.*
> *So them to myself I have to keep.*

I believe that Flic Tamworth works in publishing so do not be surprised if you see a volume or two of my verse on the shelves at Waterstone's 'ere long.

I see very little of Fou Fou Latte as she is working all the hours of the day for Goldmans. I fear that she is not a natural City creature, despite being my daughter. Her grasp of the market is pretty hopeless and she said to me only last week that she thought it would be wise for me, and indeed everyone, to sell equity and go liquid before too long. The dear girl is still very young and naïve; I have never seen such favourable signs for investment and I am piling in. She has found time to date a young man but is desperately secretive about the affair and will not let me vet the chap. I hope he is up to scratch as too many girls give themselves to opinionated wastrels who never live up to much. The flat in Fulham is delightful but either Fou Fou must employ a cleaner or she will have to spend an hour a day tidying the place as I have high standards of hygiene.

Kensington found God at the beginning of the summer and has set up a group called the 'Blewbury Believers'. They meet three times a week but have recently suffered a blow as the lead from off their church roof has been stolen. Kensie travels up to London periodically and preaches at many services. I have been to listen to him once and am proud of his oratorical skills but gave him a pointer or two as to how he might improve his delivery. I might drop a note on the same subject to our new Prime Minister. Anyway, the congregations to whom K talks will reap the benefit of my tips.

Kyle is now five and a strapping young lad. I worry about the standards that Mabel and his father are setting him as his language is distinctly coarse; I am not, nor ever will be, 'a blithering idiot of a toss pot'. He has been at school for over a year but his attendance record is poor and I would like to know precisely what he was suspended for. His parents have been evasive and mumble about knife culture; well, if the boy does not know how to behave at meal times, it is the responsibility of his school to teach him. I wish you all a wonderful holiday.

Alasdair and (sometimes) FFL

An Area in which She has Made the Wrong Decisions.

2008

Financially things have been difficult. I am, however, a man who is full of resourcefulness and despite the huge losses that the collapse of the stockmarket has inflicted upon me, I have ideas. At present I choose not to divulge all of them to you but I can reveal that one of them is that the time has come for Fou Fou Latte to start repaying me a lifetime of debt. She has been extraordinarily fortunate to have survived the year with wealth fully secure. I talked in last year's letter of her reading of the economic climate and by some lucky fluke she has been proved right. Now she must look after her old man as he has lovingly cared for her in the past. Her first mistake in this respect has been to resign—just last month—from Goldman Sachs. She had been bleating for months about wanting a job that 'gives succour to the poor rather than filling the wallets of the rich'. I told her repeatedly that the poor should have worked harder at school, gained some decent examination results and then they would have found themselves in highly lucrative jobs. It is that simple. The girl elected to ignore my advice and is back in her charity mode and is working for Macmillan Nurses. I cannot believe just how selfish and, I suspect, lazy she is! I have been the ideal rôle model over the years: an English gentleman who lives for others whilst still bringing home the bacon. Has she learnt nothing?

Fou Fou Latte has disappointed me and her romantic life has been another area in which she has made the wrong decisions. It transpired that the man with whom she had a meaningful relationship last year was a Royal, and no minor one at that, let me tell you. I can divulge nothing of his identity, but let it suffice to say that his mother and I were nearly engaged ourselves. And no, he doesn't have red hair. Yet Fou Fou has been harping on about true love and has thus catastrophically abandoned her young prince, despite my loud and forceful remonstrations.

Such behaviour would be bad enough but she has compounded her

---

*Named, I believe, after the great Labour Prime Minister, Harold Macmillan.

folly twofold by beginning a sordid dalliance with a man who says 'pardon' and 'toilet'. I admit that he is charming, handsome and successful but I ask you: 'pardon' and 'toilet'! She is now based back in the Oxford area and has put Lilyville Road up for sale. Her offer of accommodation in her house on Boar's Hill is all very well but she appears to have forgotten that I am no country hick; I need the energy of the big city to motivate me. FFL has had a poor 12 months and if I were to write a school report for her, it would read something like this: 'Fou Fou Latte has had a poor 12 months.' My reports were always pithy, witty and to the point.

Whilst I have seen the value of my investments dwindle to almost nothing, my own career has been moving forward apace. I now deliver leaflets four days a week for a variety of businesses and have a terrific technique with letterboxes which enables me to complete an average street faster than before by up to two minutes. This is rewarding work. Nevertheless I have continued to scan papers for teaching jobs and only last month was down to the final ten for the post of Classics master in a reputable preparatory school. My interview was a *'tower de force'* and my demonstration lesson on the eruption of Etna at Pompei was a triumph. It is a sad indictment of the ageism of this country that I was not appointed. It is good to know, however, that my teaching gifts are undiminished.

News from the country is mixed. Poor Kensington has again had a troubled spell and was charged, tried and convicted of stealing lead from church roofs. This strikes me as the decision of an aged and out of touch judge. Kensington is a born-again Christian; would he really do things on his own doorstep or indeed rooftop? I think not. Kyle has reacted badly to his father's imprisonment and has been asked to leave his school after—allegedly—hitting his teacher with a cricket bat. (Were this the case, I hope it was a cover drive.) If I do have to return to the country, I may well have to put my pedagogic genius to use with Kyle. Gribley told me on the telephone recently that the Duke and Ricky are little rogues who are rampaging through the terrible twos. They literally need, as I told John, a damn good thrashing. Norm, Melissa and John are extremely happy together and are offering me an absurdly low price for my Aldworth home—I will never ever sell it. As for my own romantic life, it picked up in June when I had a meeting with Flic Tamworth about my collection of quality verse. Over dinner I could sense that there was magic in the air but when I mentioned this to her, she very professionally said that with me she could not mix business and pleasure. I am not certain when the poems will be published as Flic has not yet got back to me but it will be a red letter day. Alasdaira has proved an ungrateful little girl and has not written to me once since I had to relocate. I, on the other hand, tried to contact her several times, as I needed to know the address of her eye surgeon whom, I hope, may well perform a laser operation to improve my failing sight. I think that the time has come for me to disown her.

Samantha, my ex-wife, has had a child with Simon Turquet, my ex-friend, and you may have seen Jonathan Derdle on Question Time. It is only because Cameron loves Old Etonians that Derdle's star appears to be in the ascendant. I could not help noticing in the Queen's Birthday Honours that Graham Davison has been awarded a knighthood for services to education. That should have been mine. I have to stop now as my Chicken Korma from Tesco is ready to come out of the microwave. I have never been happier.

Alasdair

The Roseman Festivities should be Fun

2009

Voici je, le grand Ros, que passe la majorité de 2009 à France! France et tres content! I would continue 'Ma Noel letter' in French but I know that those less linguistically talented than I might quickly lose the thread of what has been the greatest adventure of my life so far. As last year dawned, I chanced upon Éloise Dublanc at a recycling centre near Fou Fou Latte's home above the dreaming spires. My first thought was that she must be there in the mistaken belief that they could do something about her sagging chin and unfortunate crow's feet! 'Tu veut recycler toi?' I called out to her humorously with a cheery wave. We fell into easy conversation and she in her rather gauche★ way suggested that I must be frustrated delivering leaflets. She actually had the nerve to aver that the job had left me looking jaded. Jaded? Moi! How little she understands the joys of life in the fresh air! Scarcely aweek later the besotted woman, who clearly has never got over me, was on the phone with the following proposition: her nephew, Head of a Lycée in Meaux near Paris had been let down by an unreliable English student, so needed a language assistant. I told Éloise that I would need some time to consider the offer as it would mean the end of a successful career in leafleting. She agreed to allow me an opportunity to mull things over. So we talked about old acquaintances for a couple of minutes before I accepted her exciting offer.

What a time I have had since then! Meaux, I confess, has its drawbacks; the principal one is that it smells horribly of a combination of mustard, Brie and Frenchmen. We ex-patriots are fortunately a hardy and inventive band of brothers and I have learnt to stand well away from *Les Monsieurs* I meet and to raise the volume of my voice to communicate with them. The school is, mercifully, only too well aware of what a prodigiously gifted *prof* they have landed and have provided me with delightful accommodation commensurate to one of my educational

★Unsophisticated, as in the Rive Gauche in Paris

status. I have a very chic bedsit with a basin and a portable gas stove which enables me to organise barbecues (I am still the Gourmet at the Grill!) in the communal garden. If any of you find yourself passing through Meaux on the first Monday of every odd month of the year, do join M. Onuyeur and me at our regular *grand repas. Si vous plais!*

My oral lessons are the highlight of the week for the French children. They struggle to cope with the complexities of the English language and so I have to explain its workings in French. Their happy grins and merry laughter as I do so, show what satisfaction they derive from the acquisition of knowledge. We teachers have a heavy responsibility to bear. My students have become like friends and hail me in the street to invite me to share *un biere*. How we laugh as we trade stories! Our language of communication does, I fear, have to be French but I suspect that those who enjoy a second year of my tutelage will soon be gabbling away in Shakespeare's tongue.

Éloise has been out to visit me an absurd number of times—she can't get enough!—and on every occasion has brought Fou Fou Latte with her. I have taken it upon myself to show them all the sights of the town. When the *cafés* close at 7 we have occasionally trooped into Paris and made the pilgrimage to that underpass whose siren call I find so hard to resist. FFL has become a worry for me as I fear she is lonely and perhaps lovesick for her prince. She has repeatedly asked me to leave France and join her in Oxford. She is being just a teensy bit selfish but that is her mother's genes for you! In June she came out and dragged me along to Roland Garros where we saw young Federer triumph. As I said to Fou Fou, those tennis artistes amongst us rejoice in his victory.

Kensington has been released from jail, I gather, and has become a dealer in some form of commodity. FFL was, it seemed, uncertain as to the precise nature of the goods he handles but I suspect that it is probably coffee. I hope that he will ring me as he could benefit from my financial nous and wizardry. Now that I am so settled in France I have sold the Aldworth estate (nearly at the top of the market) to Gribley and his gang and with some of the proceeds I intend to self-publish the first volume of

my verse. I did invite John to bring le Duc and Ric on *'une petite tour de France'* as they need the influence of their father. He sadly declined as the purchase of the house has left him short of funds; I make it a rule of thumb to drive a hard bargain even when family and dear friends are involved.

Christmas this year is going to be a splendid affair as I have invited the entire staff of the school to drinks *'Cher moi'*. Yuletide is a special time and I want my froggy friends to experience a little English hospitality. It is a shame that Claude Onuyeur cannot make it but the rest of us will share in a dose of *entente cordial*. If any of you find yourselves passing this way on the 24th perhaps you will join the Roseman festivities! It should be fun.

I plan to have a Karaoke night and have been rehearsing Wacko Jacko hits since his demise in the summer. The Jackson & Roseman versions are, I am confident, almost indistinguishable although my moonwalk is definitely superior.

l'Alasdair

THE RETURN VIA HEATHROW

2010

Dear Heather,

I don't think that you'll remember me personally but Alasdair Roseman has probably mentioned my name a few times in his Christmas letters. I am Fou Fou Latte and am at present looking after him in my house near Oxford. The poor man has suffered a nervous breakdown and is very confused and morose. Things have not been going very well with him for years now and the loss of his job in France was compounded by his failure to be re-employed as a leaflet distributor here. It hit him very hard. I decided that I would write to all those to whom he sends his Christmas letter to let them know how things stand but it appears that recently only you have been sent a copy that has not been returned. I know he would love to see you as it would remind him of happier times. I hope you had a wonderful Christmas and a very happy New Year.

    Yours sincerely,

    Fou Fou Latte Gribley